HEINEMANN MODULAR MATHEMATICS
for
EDEXCEL AS AND A-LEVEL
Statistics 1

Greg Attwood

Endorsed by **edexcel** ▦

heinemann.co.uk
✓ Free online support
✓ Useful weblinks
✓ 24 hour online ordering

01865 888058

Heinemann
Inspiring generations

Heinemann Educational Publishers,
Halley Court, Jordan Hill, Oxford, OX2 8EJ
Part of Harcourt Education

Heinemann is the registered trademark of
Harcourt Education Limited

08 07 06

17

10-digit ISBN: 0 435510 82 7
13-digit ISBN: 978 0 435510 82 4

Cover design by Gecko Limited

Original design by Geoffrey Wadsley; additional design work by Jim Turner

Typeset and illustrated by Tech-Set Limited, Gateshead, Tyne and Wear.

Printed in China by China Translation & Printing Services Ltd.

Acknowledgements:

The publisher's and authors' thanks are due to Edexcel for permission to
reproduce questions from past examination papers. These are marked with an [E].
   The answers have been provided by the authors and are not the responsibility
of the examining board.

The publishers would also like to thank Edexcel for permission to reproduce the
following mathematical tables:
Table 1 The Normal distribution function,
Table 2 Percentage points of the Normal distribution.

About this book

This book is designed to provide you with the best preparation possible for your Edexcel S1 exam. The series authors are senior examiners and exam moderators themselves and have a good understanding of Edexcel's requirements.

Use this **new edition** to prepare for the new 6-unit specification. Use the first edition (*Heinemann Modular Mathematics for London AS and A-Level*) if you are preparing for the 4-module syllabus.

Finding your way around

To help to find your way around when you are studying and revising use the:

- **edge marks** (shown on the front page) – these help you to get to the right chapter quickly;
- **contents list** – this lists the headings that identify key syllabus ideas covered in the book so you can turn straight to them;
- **index** – if you need to find a topic the **bold** number shows where to find the main entry on a topic.

Remembering key ideas

We have provided clear explanations of the key ideas and techniques you need throughout the book. Key ideas you need to remember are listed in a **summary of key points** at the end of each chapter and marked like this in the chapters:

$$\blacksquare \qquad \text{IQR} = Q_3 - Q_1$$

Exercises and exam questions

In this book questions are carefully graded so they increase in difficulty and gradually bring you up to exam standard.

- **past exam questions** are marked with an [E];
- **review exercises** on pages 97 and 181 help you practise answering questions from several areas of mathematics at once, as in the real exam;
- **exam style practice paper** – this is designed to help you prepare for the exam itself;
- **answers** are included at the end of the book – use them to check your work.

Contents

8 Discrete random variables

9 The normal distribution

Mathematical modelling in probability and statistics

1

1.1 What is a model?

Many people travel to work each day by train. These trains are frequently powered by electricity. They all run on a metal track and they each have a driver. You may have played with a toy train set when you were younger. The toy train would have been much smaller than the *real* train but it would have been made to look very similar to it. It too might have been powered by electricity but from a battery within the engine rather than through an extra rail by the track. The toy train probably ran on a plastic track not a metal one like a real train and might also have had a small plastic driver but this driver could not alter the speed or stop the train like the driver of a real train. Your toy train was a **model** of a real train. It was like the real train in many ways but did not have *all* the features of the real thing.

It is important to remember that a model is not the *same* as the more complicated object in the real world which it has been created to represent. When a model is created just *some aspects* of the real object are reproduced. No attempt is made to replicate the real object in every detail. A model will be a *simplification* of the real thing, it will be both *quicker and cheaper* to produce than the real one and can help us to *improve our understanding* of the real-world object. For example, a model train and track can be used to discover the effect on the train of a buckling of the track. Using a model in this way can help us to deal with problems which might arise in the real world without the expense and risk of testing them on a real train!

1.2 Mathematical modelling

In the same way that a model train can help to solve problems in the real world so a **mathematical model** can be used to find solutions to problems without the need to construct a physical model.

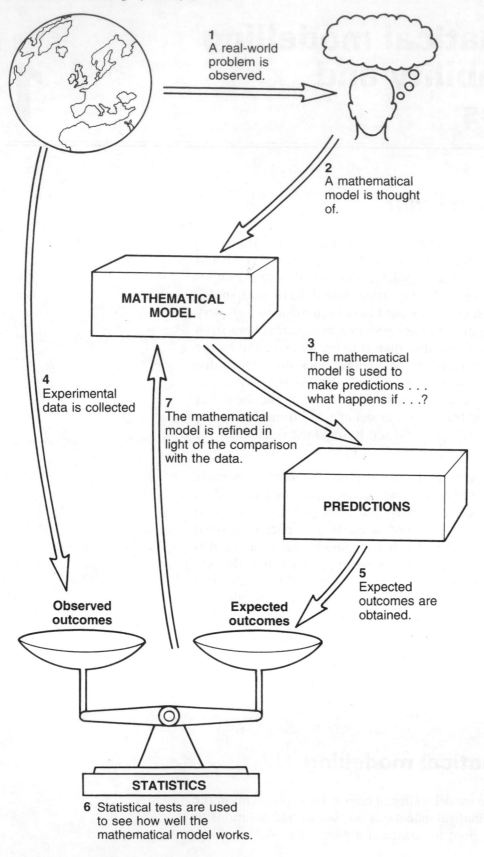

1 A real-world problem is observed.

2 A mathematical model is thought of.

MATHEMATICAL MODEL

3 The mathematical model is used to make predictions . . . what happens if . . .?

4 Experimental data is collected

7 The mathematical model is refined in light of the comparison with the data.

PREDICTIONS

5 Expected outcomes are obtained.

Observed outcomes

Expected outcomes

STATISTICS

6 Statistical tests are used to see how well the mathematical model works.

Mathematical models can be used to describe a wide variety of problems but when an element of *randomness* is involved the models require the use of **probability**. Consider the following problems:

"Will a coin land heads or tails when it is tossed or might it land on its edge?"

"How many rain drops will land on the window of your room in the next 5 minutes?"

"What are your chances of scoring a bull's eye with a single dart?"

These are the sorts of problems a probability model might be used to answer.

The processes involved in the creation of a mathematical model are illustrated opposite:

Starting from a real-world problem (**1**), a mathematical model is devised (**2**) and this is used to make predictions about the expected behaviour of the real-world problem (**3**). Some experimental data is also collected about the real-world problem (**4**) and this is used to list observed outcomes which are then compared with the expected outcomes predicted by the mathematical model (**5**). **Statistical** concepts are then used (**6**) to test whether the mathematical model describes the real-world problem well or not.

It may then be necessary to **refine** the mathematical model (**7**) to produce a better model of the real-world problem by repeating steps **3** to **5**.

As you can see, **statistics** plays a crucial role in judging how well the mathematical model describes the real-world problem. It is for this reason that a knowledge of statistics is of such importance in carrying out practical work in the sciences and social sciences.

Throughout this book, but particularly in chapter 9, there are references to the modelling process described in the diagram opposite which shows how modelling fits into the subjects of probability and statistics.

Representation of sample data

2

2.1 Defining types of data

Every day we are faced with a variety of statistics produced from data collected by different agencies:

"The latest Audit Bureau of Circulation's figures for July to December 1993 show the *Times Higher Education Supplement's* circulation up 12.5 per cent on the same period in 1992 and 21.8 per cent up on 1991." – *THES*, 4 March 1994.

"Colleges in the Northern Region are expecting an increase of 5.9 per cent in full-time equivalent enrolments (FTEs) between 1992–93 and 1993–94." – *FEFC Northern Region News*, March 1994.

"He produces some good statistics: 400 000 acres, land the size of Surrey, are now covered in lawns rolling out like fitted carpet, harvesting more than 55 million tons of grass cuttings a year." – *Radio Times*, 9 April 1994.

But what is data? One dictionary defines data as "a series of observations, measurements or facts". So to obtain data we have to observe or measure something. This something is known as a **variable**. For example, shoe size, weight, and nationality are all variables as we can obtain a series of observations or measurements for each of them:

Variable	*Measurement or observation*
Shoe size	6, $6\frac{1}{2}$, 7, $7\frac{1}{2}$
Weight	8.21 kg, 7.9 kg, 0.5 kg
Nationality	British, French, German

Considering these variables and their measurements or observations reveals important differences between them. Shoe size and weight are both variables whose measurements are *numerical* but the observations on nationality are *non-numerical*. So shoe size and weight are both called **quantitative** variables as their measurements take the form of **numbers** (such as size $7\frac{1}{2}$) or **quantities** (such as 8.21 kg). Nationality is called a **qualitative** variable as numerical values cannot be assigned to it in the way that they can with shoe size or weight. With nationality and other qualitative variables it is necessary to use **non-numerical descriptors** (such as British) to represent the different possible observations within the variable.

Although now generally used as a singular noun, data is properly a plural and throughtout this book it is used in this way, for example: 'these data'.

Example 1

For each of the following variables state whether they are **quantitative** or **qualitative** and give three possible measurements or observations of the variable:

(a) height   (b) eye colour   (c) age
(d) distance from college   (e) town of birth

(a) Height is a **quantitative** variable and three possible values are 72 inches, 6 feet 2 inches, and 1.76 metres.

(b) Eye colour is a **qualitative** variable and three possible observations are blue, green, and hazel.

(c) Age is a **quantitative** variable and three possible values are 9 months, 2 years, and 4 years 7 months.

(d) Distance from college is a **quantitative** variable and three possible values are $\frac{3}{4}$ mile, $2\frac{1}{2}$ miles and 4.2 kilometres.

(e) Town of birth is a **qualitative** variable and three possible observations are Derby, Bath and Whitby.

Although the variables shoe size and weight are both quantitative variables as both are given numerical values, there is a difference in the way in which measurements on these two quantitative variables are recorded. When you buy a pair of shoes you can ask for a size 5 or $5\frac{1}{2}$, but *not* for a size 6.27. But when you measure someone's weight you can record it as 92.509 kg (if your scales are that accurate) even though that person may say they weigh $92\frac{1}{2}$ kg.

Weight is called a **continuous** variable as it can take any value within a given range. Shoe size is called a **discrete** variable as it can only take particular values. These values are discrete (meaning separate) from one another, so the variable is not continuous – it changes in steps.

You need to be able to distinguish between these different types of variables as the type of variable influences the method you can use to analyse data.

Example 2

State whether each of the following variables is **discrete** or **continuous**:

(a) time   (b) cost in £ and p   (c) volume   (d) height
(e) number of children in family.

(a) Time is **continuous**.

(b) Cost in £ and p is **discrete**.

(c) Volume is **continuous**.

(d) Height is **continuous**.

(e) Number of children in a family is **discrete**.

The rest of this chapter is about summarising data once it has been collected. Two forms of summary are covered in this book, one graphical and the other numerical. This chapter covers graphical summaries. Numerical summaries are covered in Chapters 3 and 4.

Before considering some graphical summaries it is worth asking why we need to summarise data which has been collected. In simple terms it is because most samples of data are too large for us to handle in their raw form. If you left this data in its raw form you would be unlikely to recognise the important features that are revealed when the data has been summarised. One reason for taking a sample is to be able to make deductions about the population from which the sample has been taken. To do this you need to analyse the data you have collected. One way of doing this is by means of graphical and numerical summaries.

The purpose of these summaries is to condense data to reveal patterns and to enable comparisons to be made. Summarising data can lead to a loss of accuracy so that any calculations based on summarised data could be less accurate than calculations based on the raw data. You may already know some methods of summarising data. If so, this chapter will be useful revision.

2.2 Frequency distributions

This set of observations shows the number of times that each of the students in a year 13 class is late during a term.

```
0  7  6   4  10   1   8   9  10   9
3  9  6   2   8   1   2   1   2   3
7  8  1   8   7   1  10   6   2   5
7  1  8   1   3   4   1   1   4   5
7  1  0  10   4   7   2   5   3   7
0  5  0   7   7   2   9   1   7   8
```

Even after several minutes studying the data it is not easy to see any pattern or to be able to answer a question such as 'How many students were late on more than 6 occasions?' Condensing the data (grouping it into a smaller number of categories) makes it easier to understand. A frequency distribution does this for these data. It is produced by making a tally chart like this:

Times absent	Tally of number of students	Frequency	Cumulative frequency
0	1111	4	4
1	ⅢⅠ ⅢⅠ 1	11	15
2	ⅢⅠ 1	6	21
3	1111	4	25
4	1111	4	29
5	1111	4	33
6	111	3	36
7	ⅢⅠ ⅢⅠ	10	46
8	ⅢⅠ 1	6	52
9	1111	4	56
10	1111	4	60
Total		60	

Each observation is represented by a tally mark placed against the appropriate category. A group of five observations is represented by ⅢⅠ making it easier to add the tallies. The tally marks for each category are totalled to give the frequency for that category.

From the frequency distribution it is possible to see any patterns that emerge. For example, in this case there are those students who missed very few classes and those who tended to be more persistent absentees.

The **cumulative frequency** for the **figures** in the table are obtained by adding the frequencies as we go down the column of frequencies:

$4, 4 + 11, 4 + 11 + 6$, and so on, giving $4, 15, 21 \ldots$

These show, for example, that there were 25 students who were absent on fewer than 4 occasions.

2.3 Cumulative frequency step polygon

Although you will not be tested on this topic in the S1 examination, it is sometimes useful to represent a cumulative frequency distribution graphically. For discrete data you can do this by drawing a **cumulative frequency step polygon**. Look at the data on absences in the table on the previous page. You can see from the table that:

students could not be absent on fewer than zero occasions

4 students were never absent

15 students were absent on fewer than two occasions.

So the graph **steps** from 4 to 15 as there were no values between zero and one. Here is the cumulative frequency step polygon for the table:

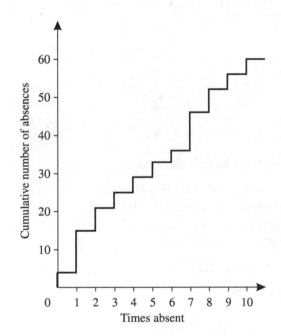

2.4 Stem and leaf diagrams

Another way to order and present data is by means of a stem and leaf diagram. Here is some data:

$$60 \quad 51 \quad 53 \quad 42 \quad 45 \quad 42 \quad 51 \quad 65 \quad 62 \quad 50$$

And here is a stem and leaf diagram to represent these numbers:

stem ⟶ 4 | 2 5 2 ⟵ leaves

5 | 1 3 1 0

6 | 0 5 2

Each digit to the left of the vertical line is a stem. The digits on the right of the vertical line are the leaves associated with the stems. For the first row 4 2 5 2 the stem is 4 and the leaves are 2, 5 and 2. This row represents the numbers 42, 45 and 42. This stem and leaf diagram has been created by splitting each number into two parts in which the tens digit becomes the stem and the units digit the leaf.

Once the data has been ordered into stems and leaves it is usual to re-draw the diagram so that the leaves are in numerical order like this.

4	2 2 5
5	0 1 1 3
6	0 2 5

This allows the stem and leaf diagram to be used in calculations.

Sometimes the data being represented by a stem and leaf diagram are not integer data. The stem and leaf diagram is prepared in the same way, but a note is included on the diagram to ensure it is read correctly. For example, the following heights in centimetres:

4.2, 4.7, 5.1, 6.2, 5.3, 5.7, 5.9, 4.4, 5.9, 6.1, 5.9, 6.4, 5.2

can be shown on a stem and leaf diagram like this:

Height in cm   4 | 2 means 4.2

4	2 4 7
5	1 2 3 7 9 9 9
6	1 2 4

As you can see, only two significant figures can be represented on a stem and leaf diagram, so it may be necessary to round data to meet this constraint. For example, 7.27 and 8.322 would need to be rounded to 7.3 and 8.3 to allow them to be represented on a stem and leaf diagram.

In some diagrams a large number of leaves are associated with one stem. Then it is usual to use two lines for that stem to improve the display of the data.

Stem and leaf diagrams have the advantage over bar charts and similar representations that the shape of the distribution of the data can be seen without losing the detail of the original data. For example, in the height data there are clearly more observations between 5.0 and 5.9 cm than between 4.0 and 4.9 or between 6.0 and 6.9 as the number of leaves for the '5' stem is greatest. Each data value between 5.0 and 5.9 can still be read directly from the diagram: 5.1, 5.2 and so on.

Example 3

Over a period of time Mendit Ltd a motor repair company records the time, x minutes to the nearest minute, taken to carry out a particular type of repair. The values of x recorded for 51 repairs are given below. Construct a stem and leaf diagram for these data:

```
33  38  34  46  42  36  41
43  41  46  41  30  51  36
37  33  24  36  31  31  24
51  34  42  50  21  56  32
34  34  46  43  62  34  32
45  30  31  36  39  37  56
31  47  40  40  55  42  30
30  62
```

Here is the unordered stem and leaf diagram produced by working down the columns. It is equally acceptable to work along the rows, since the ordered stem and leaf diagram will be the same for both.

Repair times		2	4 means 24
2	4 1 4		(3)
3	3 7 4 1 0 8 3 4 4 0 4 1 6 6 0 1 9 6 1 4 7 6 2 2 0		(25)
4	3 5 1 7 6 2 6 0 6 1 3 0 2 2 1		(15)
5	1 0 5 1 6 6		(6)
6	2 2		(2)

Notice that you can improve the diagram by showing the number of leaves on each stem. These are shown in brackets. This is also a way of checking that all leaves have been accounted for.

Reordering and splitting the data into two parts for stems 3 and 4 gives:

Repair times		2	1 means 21
2	1 4 4		(3)
3	0 0 0 0 1 1 1 1 2 2 3 3 4 4 4 4 4		(17)
3	6 6 6 6 7 7 8 9		(8)
4	0 0 1 1 1 2 2 2 3 3		(10)
4	5 6 6 6 7		(5)
5	0 1 1 5 6 6		(6)
6	2 2		(2)

Back-to-back stem and leaf diagrams

If direct comparison of two data sets is required, it can be achieved by placing the stem and leaf diagrams 'back-to-back' rather than keeping them as separate diagrams.

Example 4

There are 24 children in class A. Each child is given the same problem to solve. The time each child takes to solve it is recorded to the nearest tenth of a minute:

$$7.4 \quad 8.2 \quad 6.1 \quad 9.3 \quad 7.4 \quad 8.5 \quad 7.2 \quad 6.8$$
$$6.4 \quad 7.7 \quad 9.6 \quad 8.8 \quad 8.9 \quad 7.2 \quad 7.3 \quad 7.0$$
$$5.9 \quad 8.9 \quad 7.6 \quad 9.3 \quad 7.4 \quad 7.9 \quad 9.1 \quad 5.7$$

The 27 children in class B are also given the same problem and their times for solving it are:

$$8.2 \quad 7.3 \quad 6.9 \quad 5.5 \quad 6.1 \quad 9.3 \quad 8.1 \quad 7.2 \quad 7.7$$
$$6.7 \quad 7.6 \quad 8.4 \quad 8.8 \quad 5.8 \quad 6.9 \quad 8.2 \quad 9.5 \quad 9.1$$
$$5.4 \quad 6.4 \quad 7.7 \quad 5.2 \quad 7.1 \quad 6.6 \quad 5.9 \quad 6.7 \quad 6.0$$

Represent these data using a 'back-to-back' stem and leaf diagram. Use the diagram to compare the times of the two classes.

Here are unordered and ordered stem and leaf diagrams for the two classes.

Class A

Unordered				Ordered			
Time to solve problem	5	9 means 5.9		Time to solve problem	5	7 means 5.7	
5	9 7		(2)	5	7 9		(2)
6	1 8 4		(3)	6	1 4 8		(3)
7	4 4 2 7 2 3 0 6 4 9		(10)	7	0 2 2 3 4 4 4 6 7 9		(10)
8	2 5 8 9 9		(5)	8	2 5 8 9 9		(5)
9	3 6 3 1		(4)	9	1 3 3 6		(4)

Class B

Unordered			Ordered		
Time to solve problem	5	5 means 5.5	Time to solve problem	5	2 means 5.2
5	5 8 4 2 9	(5)	5	2 4 5 8 9	(5)
6	9 1 7 9 4 6 7 0	(8)	6	0 1 4 6 7 7 9 9	(8)
7	3 2 7 6 7 1	(6)	7	1 2 3 6 7 7	(6)
8	2 1 4 8 2	(5)	8	1 2 2 4 8	(5)
9	3 5 1	(3)	9	1 3 5	(3)

The 'back-to-back' diagram can now be drawn:

Time to solve problem

	Class A		Class B	5|2 means 5.2
(2)	9 7	5	2 4 5 8 9	(5)
(3)	8 4 1	6	0 1 4 6 7 7 9 9	(8)
(10)	9 7 6 4 4 4 3 2 2 0	7	1 2 3 6 7 7	(6)
(5)	9 9 8 5 2	8	1 2 2 4 8	(5)
(4)	6 3 3 1	9	1 3 5	(3)

This back-to-back diagram shows that the children in class B tend to solve the problem in a shorter time than those in class A.

Exercise 2A

1   During the months of June and July a gardener noted the temperature in °C each day at noon. The results are shown below. Construct a frequency distribution for these data:

$$
\begin{array}{cccccccc}
18 & 20 & 20 & 21 & 22 & 21 & 22 & 20 \\
22 & 19 & 21 & 19 & 23 & 24 & 19 & 20 \\
19 & 22 & 22 & 20 & 20 & 20 & 21 & 21 \\
20 & 20 & 21 & 22 & 21 & 21 & 23 & 24 \\
21 & 20 & 20 & 19 & 22 & 23 & 24 & 25 \\
25 & 26 & 27 & 27 & 26 & 24 & 22 & 19 \\
18 & 18 & 20 & 22 & 24 & 25 & 23 & 22 \\
20 & 24 & 25 & 25 & 27 & & &
\end{array}
$$

2   At the beginning of term a school held a disco. The next day a random sample of 50 of those who attended were asked to rate the disco on a five point scale A, B, C, D, E where A represents maximum enjoyment and E minimum enjoyment. Their ratings are shown below. Construct a frequency distribution for these ratings:

$$
\begin{array}{cccccccccc}
A & C & E & C & C & E & A & C & B & C \\
E & C & B & B & A & B & C & B & D & D \\
D & B & D & B & B & B & C & B & C & C \\
E & B & B & B & D & A & B & A & B & B \\
C & D & C & E & B & D & C & C & D & D
\end{array}
$$

3 The results of the GCSE mock examination in mathematics for Year 11 in 1993 at a school are shown below. Construct a stem and leaf diagram to represent these data:

42 54 80 48 73 50 59 45 84 49
67 47 70 78 77 67 55 88 42 59
54 41 69 65 41 86 80 89 44 68
82 41 71 42 85 84 51 69 89 72
72 46 85 40 78 67 66 52 42 89
86 41 62 51 73 50 41 58 44 69

4 A busy filling station records the number of motorists who buy diesel fuel for their cars each day. The number on 50 consecutive days is shown below. Construct a stem and leaf diagram to represent these data:

28 19 17 30 45 37 43 36 36 12
13 17 12 27 10 17 23 23 9 10
 9 14 15 8 26 30 26 22 19 20
28 19 32 21 23 26 34 16 17 18
33 26 28 31 30 22 21 21 15 19

5 A gardener is making a fence for his garden. He purchases a large number of pieces of wood, all of them longer than 100 cm in length. Each piece is then cut so that it is 100 cm long. The lengths of the 'off-cuts' in cm resulting from cutting the lengths to size are given below. Construct a stem and leaf diagram to represent these data:

5.2 6.6 4.3 8.3 5.1 7.5 8.6 7.1 7.8 2.2
6.6 5.8 3.5 7.5 6.1 3.8 2.5 2.7 8.8 4.8
3.5 4.3 6.1 5.6 5.2 8.8 6.4 6.4 3.8 8.1
8.9 3.5 7.6 3.1 7.2 3.4 7.8 8.4 4.7 7.7
7.5 6.8 7.5 8.3 6.2 6.7 5.2 3.7 8.6 5.2
7.3 2.5 4.7 7.6 2.7 5.1 5.2 3.2 3.2 6.4

6 The data below records the numbers of days a sample of patients had to wait before they were able to see their hospital consultant. Construct a stem and leaf diagram to represent these data:

```
55  46  36  49  20  59  48  54  35  34
31  44  52  46  33  52  51  22  43  47
29  28  29  57  17  38  25  10  38  16
39  44  15  57  25  14  51  38  17  49
56  19  45  51  21  37  44  19  45  21
29  52  28  32  57  35  53  25  42  14
```

7 At the same school described in question **3** the results of the GCSE mock examination in mathematics for year 11 in 1994 were as follows:

```
45  69  56  43  72  76  43  40  66  77
30  50  32  62  63  47  42  76  47  32
52  43  60  63  43  31  37  43  30  52
66  70  71  32  32  50  45  56  48  38
60  45  47  35  54  34  73  63  49  47
52  49  48  40  42
```

Use these data and that in question **3** to construct a 'back-to-back' stem and leaf diagram. Comment on your results.

8 Over a period of 40 school days the school shop recorded the number of packets of crisps bought each day by boys and girls at the school. The results were as follows:

Girls							Boys					
10	16	35	29	30	11	18	17	32	37	42	20	41	11
13	33	13	10	32	40	25	40	25	10	32	39	34	31
27	25	18	38	43	26	44	49	47	17	14	26	36	29
24	39	44	29	11	23	19	42	22	19	42	38	20	28
42	36	21	16	31	32	41	24	44	34	20	41	28	48
48	34	28	11	27			46	26	28	42	22		

Construct a 'back-to-back' stem and leaf diagram to represent these data. Comment on your results.

2.5 Grouped frequency distributions

When you need to summarise a large sample of data, the frequency distribution or stem and leaf diagram may not be appropriate. Instead you can use an alternative summary called a **grouped frequency distribution**. This involves tabulating the frequencies associated with *groups* of observations rather than single observations.

Here is a large sample of observations. It shows the number of visits to the doctor made by each of 150 patients during one year.

```
 3   2   6   2   6   5  22   3   1  10
 5   9   7   2   5   1   5   4   9   7
25  19   8   2   5   8  10  16  15   5
 7   8   3   6   6  21   6   9   4   5
 6   6  22   8  11  23   8   5   9   6
 8   7  15  10  16  11  13   1   7   3
 2  18   0  16   4   9   8   5   9  17
 7   9   5  19  12   1  10   3   5   7
13  18   8   7   8   7   7  13   0   5
14   7  20   1   9   4   6  24   9   6
11   5   6  28   7   7  22   1  17   4
11   8   1   4  12  13   9  23  14   5
 2   6   6  11   3  14   6   8   4   4
 6   8  29  18   5   8   8  17   4   4
 5  18   7   3  11  23  20  10   6   6
```

A frequency distribution for these data would give the table of 30 lines shown here. This is not a very useful summary.

Only the start and end of the table are shown.

Visits	Frequency
0	2
1	7
.	.
.	.
28	1
29	1

This table can be condensed even more to produce a grouped frequency distribution:

Visits	Frequency	Cumulative frequency
0–4	32	32
5–9	71	103
10–14	20	123
15–19	14	137
20–24	10	147
25–29	3	150
Total	150	

The cumulative frequency has been included as it will be needed later.

Deciding on the number of groups and the width of the groups in a grouped frequency distribution is up to the person producing it. There are no definite rules to help make such decisions but here are two useful guidelines:

■ Aim to have as few groups as is reasonable; too many, and little advantage is gained over a frequency distribution; too few, and patterns in the data will not be revealed. Somewhere between 5 and 15 groups, with 10 being about right, can be used as a 'rule of thumb'.

■ Use this 'rule of thumb' to estimate the class width:

$$\text{class width} = \frac{\text{largest value} - \text{smallest value}}{\text{number of groups}}$$

You need to use this rule of thumb sensibly. For example, if the largest value in a distribution is 579, the smallest value is 500 and 10 groups are required then

$$\text{class width} = \frac{579 - 500}{10} = 7.9$$

Rather than use 7.9 as the class width you might use 8, or more likely for ease of tabulation use 10. Using 10 as the width and starting at 500 (giving 500–509, 510–519) would give 8 groups rather than 10, but this still fits within the guideline of 5 to 15 groups. Remember, there are no hard and fast rules, just 'rules of thumb' to be used with a little common sense.

Although the detail of the original set of 150 observations has been lost, the data reveals its patterns and allows summaries to be made. For example, the group containing the most observations is 5–9. Another summary is that two-thirds of the patients visited the doctor fewer than 10 times during the year.

Before moving on it is worth revising the terminology of grouped frequency distributions. The groups are more usually called **classes**. Here is the class 5–9:

Class

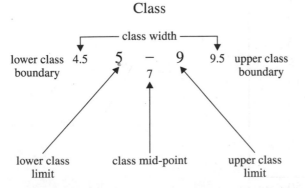

You need to remember all the terms shown in this diagram.

Example 5

Write down the class boundaries, mid-point and class width for each
of the following classes:

(a) 8–12   (b) 2.5–3.4   (c) (−3)–(+3)

	Class boundaries	Mid-point	Class width
(a)	7.5, 12.5	$\frac{1}{2}(7.5 + 12.5) = 10$	$12.5 - 7.5 = 5$
		or	
		$\frac{1}{2}(8 + 12) = 10$	
(b)	2.45, 3.45	2.95	1.00
(c)	−3.5, 3.5	0	7

Example 6

The height x millimetres, to the nearest millimetre, of each of a
number of seedlings was measured before each one was transplanted
into an individual pot. The heights recorded for a sample of 50
seedlings were:

```
31  36  40  37  28  23  13  44  25  28
46  33  33  31  42  32  53  30  24  35
31  17  20  41  30  41  31  41  18  49
46  39  29  27  39  26  43  21  31  35
38  34  37  33  21  34  38  28  33  27
```

Prepare a grouped frequency distribution for these data using equal
class widths, the first class having a lower class boundary of 9.5 and
mid-point of 12.

If the lower class boundary of the first class is 9.5, the lower class
limit is 10. If the mid-point is 12 the upper class limit must be 14. So
the grouped frequency distribution is:

Class	Frequency
10–14	1
15–19	2
20–24	5
25–29	8
30–34	14
35–39	9
40–44	7
45–49	3
50–54	1
Total	50

2.6 Cumulative frequency polygons for grouped data

In section 2.3 a cumulative frequency step polygon was used to represent the data in a frequency distribution. In a similar way the data in a grouped frequency distribution can be represented by a **cumulative frequency polygon**. In this situation the **cumulative frequencies** are plotted against the **upper class boundaries** of the corresponding classes. So for the data in section 2.5 relating to visits the plotted points are (4.5, 32), (9.5, 103), (14.5, 123) and so on. The polygon is shown below with the points joined by straight lines:

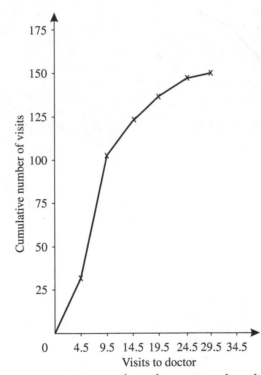

It is very important to stress that the upper class boundaries are used when plotting a cumulative frequency polygon.

Example 7

This table summarises the weights in kilograms, to the nearest 100 grams, of 250 boys:

(a) Represent these data by means of a cumulative frequency polygon.

(b) Estimate the weight which is exceeded by 20% of the boys.

Weight (kg)	Number of boys
44.0–47.9	3
48.0–51.9	17
52.0–55.9	50
56.0–57.9	45
58.0–59.9	46
60.0–63.9	57
64.0–67.9	23
68.0–71.9	9

(a) The upper class boundaries and cumulative frequencies required to draw the polygon are:

Upper class boundaries	47.95	51.95	55.95	57.95	59.95	63.95	67.95	71.95
Cumulative frequencies	3	20	70	115	161	218	241	250

Here is the cumulative frequency polygon:

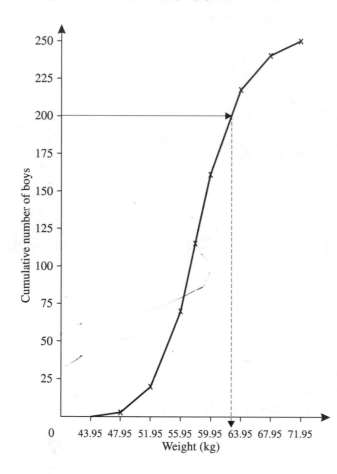

Notice that the polygon touches the horizontal axis at 43.95 as there are no boys below that boundary.

(b) 20% of 250 is 50, so the weight corresponding to 200 boys needs to be estimated from the polygon. This is done by drawing a horizontal line from the cumulative frequency of 200 and where this intersects the polygon the corresponding value (indicated by the broken line) is read from the horizontal scale.

Thus from the cumulative frequency polygon the estimate is 62.75 kg. Hence to the nearest 100 g the estimate is 62.8 kg.

2.7 Histograms

Line diagrams and bar charts are usually drawn to represent frequency distributions. These diagrams use the height of any line or bar to represent frequency.

If the data available is for a **continuous variable** and it is summarised by **a grouped frequency distribution** then the data can be represented by means of a **histogram**.

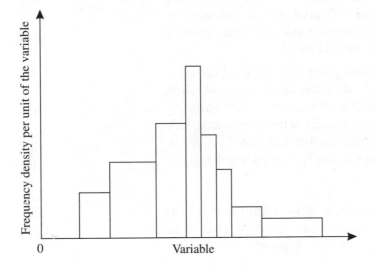

Although at a quick glance histograms look similar to bar charts there are two fundamental differences:

■ There are no gaps between the bars of a histogram

■ There is an important relationship between the area of a histogram bar and the frequency that it is representing.

For a histogram bar,

■   **Area $\propto$ Frequency**

and since the histogram consists of a series of bars, then for a histogram:

■   **Total area $\propto$ Total frequency**

This concept of area being proportional to frequency is important and distinguishes a histogram from a bar chart.

To calculate the height of each bar in a histogram use:

$$\text{Area} \propto \text{Frequency}$$

Thus: $\text{Area} = k \times \text{Frequency}$

where k is the constant of proportionality and can take any positive value. For simplicity and ease of calculation let $k = 1$.

Hence:
$$\text{Area} = \text{Frequency}$$

Therefore:
$$\text{Height of bar} \times \text{Class width} = \text{Frequency}$$

So:
$$\text{Height of bar} = \frac{\text{Frequency}}{\text{Class width}}$$

Even if all class widths are equal it is recommended that you use $k = 1$ so that the method used is consistent and the resulting histogram has an area which is always equal to the total frequency. This allows for easy reading and interpretation of histograms. A relative frequency histogram is shown on page 24. This method can help you to understand the use of area when calculating probabilities associated with continuous variables, but relative frequency histograms will not be examined in S1.

When calculating the height of the histogram bar you used the class width (i.e. upper class boundary − lower class boundary) and when plotting the histogram you also use these boundaries, thus ensuring that there are no gaps between the bars. Label the horizontal axis with the appropriate variable name and label the vertical axis 'Frequency density per unit of the variable' or more simply 'Frequency density'.

Example 8

A random sample of 250 children from a large school was taken. The height in centimetres, to the nearest cm, of each child was recorded and summarised in the table below. Represent the data by means of a histogram.

Height (cm)	130–134	135–139	140–144	145–149	150–154	155–159	160–164	165–169
Number of children	10	22	38	60	54	36	25	5

Estimate the number of children whose heights were between 142 cm and 153 cm.

Note that height is a continuous variable and can thus be represented by a histogram.

Class	Number of children	Class width	Frequency density $= \dfrac{\text{Frequency}}{\text{class width}}$
130–134	10	5	2.0
135–139	22	5	4.4
140–144	38	5	7.6
145–149	60	5	12.0
150–154	54	5	10.8
155–159	36	5	7.2
160–164	25	5	5.0
165–169	5	5	1.0

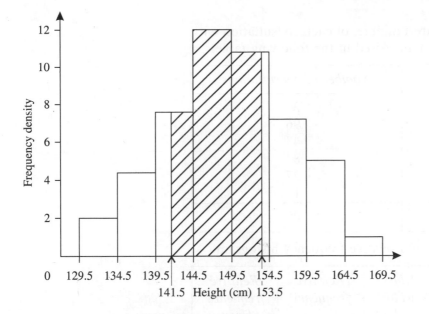

To estimate the number of children with heights between 142 cm and 153 cm, it is necessary to remember that the data are rounded up to the nearest whole number. So for estimating heights between 142 cm and 153 cm use 141.5 cm and 153.5 cm as height values when reading from the histogram.

Since Area = Frequency in this histogram then:

$$\text{Number of children} = (3 \times 7.6) + (5 \times 12) + (4 \times 10.8)$$
$$= 126$$

2.8 Relative frequency histograms

There are times when it is useful to draw a histogram based on relative frequencies rather than frequencies. The method of drawing the histogram is similar to that used in Example 8 (see page 22) with relative frequencies replacing frequencies. Relative frequencies are obtained by expressing the frequencies as a proportion of the total frequency. So using the data in Example 8 the frequencies for the classes 130–134 and 135–139 are 10 and 22 respectively. Corresponding relative frequencies are:

$$\frac{10}{250} = 0.040 \text{ and } \frac{22}{250} = 0.088$$

Example 9

The length of time, to the nearest minute, of each consultation with the doctor of 300 patients is summarised in the following table.

Time (to nearest minute)	Number of consultations
2–3	30
4	96
5	48
6–7	84
8–10	27
11–15	15
Total	300

Represent the data by means of a relative frequency histogram.

Time	Number of consultations	Class width	Relative frequency	Relative frequency density
2–3	30	2	0.10	0.05
4	96	1	0.32	0.32
5	48	1	0.16	0.16
6–7	84	2	0.28	0.14
8–10	27	3	0.09	0.03
11–15	15	5	0.05	0.01
Total	300		1.00	

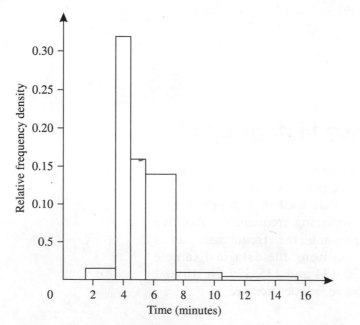

The area under this histogram is equal to 1.00 and this feature of a relative frequency histogram will prove useful later in the book.

Exercise 2B

1 Give the class boundaries, mid-point and class width for each of the following classes:

(a) 6–7   (b) 0–2   (c) 5–14   (d) (−2)–(−8)   (e) 1.50–1.75

2 The marks of 50 candidates in an examination are given below. Select suitable classes and prepare a grouped frequency distribution.

```
62  21   4  26   7  38  32  64  12  38
45   6  33  55  62  48  49   7   9  41
21  30  31   3  25  57  48   8  18  43
72  23   5   8  37  31  31  39  65  53
 4  75  17  14  61  50  51  38  36  40
```

3 Large quantities of data are often tabulated – collected together in tables. Describe two advantages and one disadvantage associated with tabulation.

4 A large number of people set out together on a fun run. The time taken by each of a sample of 50 of these people to complete the run is recorded below. The times are given to the nearest minute.

```
61  83  62  96  66  61  92  87  69  91
82  62  80  86  97  72  78  68  88  63
85  63  73  99  66  82  61  86  63  73
65  89  95  61  72  89  92  76  75  77
75  88  87  91  84  73  67  76  82  79
```

Prepare a grouped frequency distribution for these data using equal class widths, the first class having a lower limit of 60 and mid-point of 62.

5 A footwear store recorded the number of pairs of shoes sold on 52 consecutive Fridays. Here are the results:

```
60  62  94  78  73  56  64  79  54
68  66  68  71  76  67  73  67  83
87  90  93  58  46  77  37  60  74
62  40  56  59  80  69  70  69  70
70  47  54  49  63  66  66  47  51
57  53  77  68  61  98  98
```

Construct a grouped frequency distribution for these data.

6 A random sample of 50 electric bulbs were tested. Their lifetimes to the nearest hour are given below. Construct a grouped frequency distribution for these data. Draw a grouped frequency polygon to represent your distribution.

730	681	710	682	660	695	717	680	700	732
738	707	692	708	701	663	695	726	676	696
697	722	698	699	689	676	715	714	717	721
696	690	716	662	697	696	710	684	692	705
689	724	694	699	703	682	656	702	694	671

7 The heights to the nearest centimetre of a group of students are summarised below.

Height (cm)	120–129	130–139	140–149	150–159	160–169	170–179	180–189
Number of students	2	7	20	41	63	38	9

(a) Explain why it is appropriate to represent these data by a histogram rather than a bar chart.

(b) State the underlying principle involved when drawing a histogram.

(c) Draw a histogram to illustrate these data.

(d) Estimate the percentage of students with height greater than 175 cm.

8 As part of his routine examination a vet weighs to the nearest pound every dog he sees in his surgery. The following table shows the distribution of weights for a random sample of 150 dogs.

Weight (pounds)	25–29	30–34	35–39	40–44	45–49	50–54	55–59	60–64	65–69	70–74
Number of dogs	2	6	17	24	35	27	19	13	5	2

(a) Represent these data by means of a histogram.

(b) Estimate the number of dogs weighing between 41 pounds and 52 pounds inclusive.

9 A meteorologist measured the number of hours of sunshine, to the nearest hour, each day for 100 days. The results are summarised in the table below.

Hours of sunshine	Days
1	16
2–4	32
5–6	28
7	12
8	9
9–11	2
12	1

(a) On graph paper, draw a histogram to represent these data.

(b) Calculate an estimate of the number of days that had between 6 and 9 hours of sunshine. [E]

10 Telephone calls arriving at a switchboard are answered by the telephonist. The following table shows the time, to the nearest second, recorded for the telephonist to answer the calls received during one day. Represent these data by a histogram. Give a reason to justify the use of a histogram to represent these data.

Time to answer (to nearest second)	Number of calls
10–19	20
20–24	20
25–29	15
30	14
31–34	16
35–39	10
40–59	10

[E]

11 A teacher recorded the time, to the nearest minute, spent reading during a particular day by each child in a group. The times were summarised in a grouped frequency distribution and represented by a histogram. The first class in the grouped frequency distribution was 10–19 and its associated frequency was 8 children. On the histogram the height of the rectangle representing that class was 2.4 cm and the width was 2 cm. The total area under the histogram was 53.4 cm^2.
Find the number of children in the group. [E]

12 The table gives the ages, in completed years, of the population in a particular region of the United Kingdom.

Age	0–4	5–15	16–44	45–64	65–79	80 and over
Number (in thousands)	260	543	1727	756	577	135

A histogram of this data was drawn with age along the horizontal axis. The 0–4 age group was represented by a bar of horizontal width 0.5 cm and height 5.2 cm.

Find the widths and heights, in cm to 1 decimal place, of the bars representing the following age groups:

(i) 16–44   (ii) 65–79.   [E]

SUMMARY OF KEY POINTS

1 For a **stem and leaf diagram** each row represents a **stem** and is indicated by the number to the left of the vertical line. The digits to the right of the vertical line are the **leaves** associated with the stem.

2 A **grouped frequency distribution** consists of several **classes** and their associated **class frequencies.**

   For the **class 5–9** for example the

lower class boundary	is	4.5
lower class limit	is	5
upper class limit	is	9
upper class boundary	is	9.5
class width	is	$9.5 - 4.5 = 5$
class mid-point	is	$\frac{1}{2}(4.5 + 9.5) = 7$

3 When drawing a **histogram**, for each histogram bar the area is directly proportional to the frequency that it is representing:

$$\textbf{Area} \propto \textbf{Frequency}$$

   and since the histogram consists of a series of bars, then for a histogram:

$$\textbf{Total Area} \propto \textbf{Total Frequency}$$

4 The **height** of a histogram bar is found by dividing the class frequency by the class width.

5 Histograms are plotted using class boundaries.

Methods for summarising sample data (location)

3

Chapter 2 indicated that there are several graphical ways of representing data (e.g. bar charts, histograms). There are several numerical measures which can be used to summarise sample data. Some of them are single numbers used to represent a sample of data, others are used to indicate the spread of the data. The first are known as **measures of location** since they act as a *focus* for the data such that they can be used as single values to represent the whole data set. The second are known as **measures of dispersion** and are used to represent the *spread* or *variation* within the data, since it is unlikely that all the values in a data set will be the same.

3.1 Measures of location

There are several measures of location but the three most commonly used are: the **mode**, the **median** and the **arithmetic mean**. For each of these measures it is necessary to have a definition together with an explanation of how it is evaluated in practice. This evaluation will be considered for a set of raw data, a frequency distribution and a grouped frequency distribution.

It is important that you know how to calculate these three measures for each of the sets of data. However, in the S1 examination, the focus of questions will not be directed solely towards their calculation but more towards their use and interpretation. These aspects will be covered by questions at the end of chapter 4.

3.2 The mode

Consider the following set of raw data which shows the number of errors made by each of 11 secretarial students when typing the same report as part of their assessment:

$$4 \quad 6 \quad 7 \quad 5 \quad 9 \quad 10 \quad 6 \quad 6 \quad 4 \quad 7 \quad 8$$

The simplest measure used to represent these data is the **mode** which is defined as follows:

■ The MODE is that value of a variable which occurs most frequently.

In the data on the previous page you can see that the value which occurs most frequently is 6 and this is the **modal** value for these data. The mode is not always unique since some data sets may have more than one mode. For example, if a twelfth student had taken the assessment and made 4 errors then the values 4 and 6 would both have been modal values, each occurring three times. Sometimes a data set does not have a modal value and this is illustrated by the following data:

$$3 \quad 4 \quad 5 \quad 4 \quad 5 \quad 5 \quad 3 \quad 4 \quad 3$$

In this data set, each value occurs the same number of times.

The following data refer to the number of children in each of a random sample of twenty-three families. In this case the data are summarised using a frequency distribution:

Number of children	0	1	2	3	4	5
Number of families	2	5	9	4	2	1

From this distribution you can see that the modal number of children in a family is 2 since it occurs most frequently, i.e. 9 out of 23 families contain two children. It is important to make sure that you realise which is the mode (2 children) and which is the modal frequency (9 families).

In the case of a grouped frequency distribution the mode is not a particularly useful measure of location. Although there are ways of estimating the mode from a grouped frequency distribution, in this book we will restrict ourselves to using the **modal class** which is the class corresponding to the highest frequency.

The following grouped frequency distribution was used on page 16 of chapter 2 and summarises the visits to the doctor of a random sample of 150 patients:

Visits	Frequency
0–4	32
5–9	71
10–14	20
15–19	14
20–24	10
25–29	3
Total	150

For this distribution the modal class is 5–9, corresponding to the highest frequency of 71.

It is easy to appreciate that there are some advantages to be gained by using the mode to represent data since:

– it is easy to calculate
– it is not affected by any extreme value in the data set.

For example, if one of the students had performed very badly in the typing assessment on page 29 and made 32 errors, then this extreme value would not have affected the value of the mode. Unfortunately this ease of calculation is offset by the fact that the mode is not a value which has useful mathematical properties and whilst this may not seem important at this stage it will become important later in the book.

3.3 The median

The obvious advantage of using the mode to represent a set of data is the fact that it is the most frequently occurring value of the variable and since it occurs most often it is likely to be a fair representative value. Having stated that this advantage is offset by other features then we need to consider an alternative measure. Perhaps the next obvious choice is one that is in the *middle* of the data – the **median**. Before defining the median it is necessary to re-arrange the data in ascending order of magnitude. Thus the reordered data relating to the typing errors of the original eleven students on page 29 is:

$$4 \quad 4 \quad 5 \quad 6 \quad 6 \quad \mathbf{6} \quad 7 \quad 7 \quad 8 \quad 9 \quad 10$$

The definition of the median is then as follows:

■ **The MEDIAN is the middle value of an ordered set of data.**

For the above data set, containing an *odd* number of observations it is easy to see that the middle value or median is 6 (as indicated in bold type). Note that there are five values above the median and five values below it.

In general, if there are n observations, the median is the value corresponding to the $\frac{1}{2}(n+1)$th observation. Thus in this case $n = 11$ and $\frac{1}{2}(n+1) = 6$ and the sixth value is 6.

In the situation where there are an even number of observations the median is evaluated by taking half the sum of the two central values. If the 4 errors made by a twelfth student are included, the data above becomes

$$4 \quad 4 \quad 4 \quad 5 \quad 6 \quad 6 \quad 6 \quad 7 \quad 7 \quad 8 \quad 9 \quad 10$$

and the median for these data is half the sum of the sixth and seventh values. Hence:

$$\text{the median} = \frac{6+6}{2} = 6$$

If we use $\frac{1}{2}(n+1)$, then in this case:

$$\tfrac{1}{2}(n+1) = \tfrac{1}{2}(12+1) = 6\tfrac{1}{2}$$

implying a value between the sixth and seventh observations.

When considering frequency distributions in chapter 2 cumulative frequencies were introduced and these can now be used to find the median when data are summarised in a frequency distribution. Thus for the data relating to the number of children in families the table, including cumulative frequencies, is as follows:

Number of children	0	1	2	3	4	5
Number of families	2	5	9	4	2	1
Cumulative number of families	2	7	16	20	22	23

The table is a summary of the 23 ordered observations

$$0 \quad 0 \quad 1 \quad 1 \quad 1 \quad 1 \quad 1 \dots 4 \quad 4 \quad 5$$

and the median could be found as shown above. However, for data sets like this, the procedure would be tedious and it is easier to use the cumulative frequencies. Here n is 23 and so the median value corresponds to the $\frac{1}{2}(23+1)$th observation, i.e. the 12th. For these data this must be 2, since the table shows that the seventh value is 1 and the sixteenth value is 2 with all intermediate values being 2 and hence the twelfth value, the median, is equal to 2. Perhaps a 'health warning' is needed at this point. The median is **NOT $2\frac{1}{2}$** as is often suggested by students who wrongly calculate the median number of children; in this case

$$0, 1, 2, 3, 4, 5, \text{ i.e. } \tfrac{1}{2}(2+3) = 2\tfrac{1}{2}$$

This warning is introduced to try to remind you to look carefully at your final answer once you have made your evaluation. A similar warning will be issued in the next section when calculating the arithmetic mean!

You will remember that in chapter 2 when using data which has been summarised by a grouped frequency distribution the detail of the original observations was lost. This implies that any value of the median obtained from such a distribution can only be an *estimate* of the median of the original data before it was summarised. The estimate is obtained using interpolation. Consider again the table relating to visits to the doctor:

Visits	Frequency	Cumulative frequency
0–4	32	32
5–9	71	103
10–14	20	123
15–19	14	137
20–24	10	147
25–29	3	150

Since there are 150 observations the median value will be that corresponding to the $\frac{1}{2}(150+1) = 75.5$th observation, i.e. half the sum of the 75th and 76th observations. Unfortunately, because of the tabular nature of these data the values of the 75th and 76th observations are not known. However, it is known that they both lie in the class 5–9 since the first 32 observations are in the class 0–4 and the next 71 observations (including the 75th and 76th) are in the class 5–9, the **median class**. Since, as defined earlier, the median is the middle value this implies that 50% of the values are less than or equal to the median. Thus when estimating the median for a grouped frequency distribution $\frac{1}{2}n$ is used rather than $\frac{1}{2}(n+1)$.

To obtain an estimate of the median let b represent the *lower class boundary* of the median class (i.e. 4.5), f represent the sum of all the frequencies *below b* (i.e. 32), f_m represent the *frequency of the median class* (i.e. 71) and w represent the *width of the median class* (i.e. 5). Then, by interpolation, the median is given by:

$$\text{Median} = b + \left(\frac{\frac{1}{2}n - f}{f_m}\right) \times w$$

Thus for these data:

$$\text{Median} = 4.5 + \left\{\frac{75 - 32}{71}\right\} \times 5$$
$$= 7.53$$

It is important to remember that when using interpolation in this way the lower class boundary is used. It is also important to recognise that 'visits' is a discrete variable which in this situation has been treated as if it was continuous. Whilst this is not ideal it is the best solution available and, as was stated earlier, it is only an estimate.

Again it is easy to appreciate that the median shares the advantages of the mode in that:

– it is relatively easy to calculate or estimate
– it too is unaffected by extreme values since by its definition it is in the middle of the data.

Unfortunately it also shares the same disadvantage – it does not have useful mathematical properties and this leads to its restricted use.

3.4 Quantiles

The concept of dividing the data into two equal parts can be extended to dividing the data into however many equal parts you wish. The values obtained in such situations are known as **quantiles**. The most commonly used quantiles are the **quartiles** which divide the data into four equal parts. Thus we have the following definition:

■ **The QUARTILES of an ordered set of data are such that 25% of the observations are less than or equal to the first quartile (Q_1), 50% are less than or equal to the second quartile (Q_2) and 75% are less than or equal to the third quartile (Q_3).**

When evaluating the quartiles for raw data or a frequency distribution it is necessary to have a procedure which allows you to implement the above definition as accurately and meaningfully as possible. There are several approaches to this problem but the following is recommended.

Consider the n ordered observations y_1, y_2, y_3, ..., y_n. To find Q_1, first evaluate $\frac{1}{4}n$.

If $\frac{1}{4}n$ is an integer, say r, then

$$Q_1 = \tfrac{1}{2}(y_r + y_{r+1})$$

If $\frac{1}{4}n$ is not an integer but lies between the integers r and $r+1$, then

$$Q_1 = y_{r+1}$$

Similarly, to find Q_3, first evaluate $\frac{3}{4}n$ and then proceed as for Q_1.

It is worth remembering at this point that the median is Q_2 and that if you evaluate $\frac{1}{2}(n+1)$ you can then proceed as follows.

If $\frac{1}{2}(n+1)$ is an integer, say r, then

$$Q_2 = y_r$$

but if $\frac{1}{2}(n+1)$ is not an integer but lies between r and $r+1$, then

$$Q_2 = \tfrac{1}{2}(y_r + y_{r+1})$$

Alternatively, the same idea works for the median as for Q_1 and Q_3.

If $\frac{1}{2}n$ is an integer, say r, then

$$Q_2 = \tfrac{1}{2}(y_r + y_{r+1})$$

If $\frac{1}{2}n$ is not an integer but lies between the integers r and $r+1$ then

$$Q_2 = y_{r+1}$$

This gives exactly the same result.

If these procedures are applied to the data on the typing errors (4, 4, 5, 6, 6, 6, 7, 7, 8, 9, 10) then $Q_1 = 5$, $Q_2 = 6$ and $Q_3 = 8$.

For the frequency distribution relating to the number of children in the family, $n = 23$. So:

$\frac{1}{4}(23)$ $= 5.75$ $\Rightarrow Q_1$ corresponds to the 6th observation $\therefore Q_1 = 1$

$\frac{1}{2}(23 + 1) = 12$ $\Rightarrow Q_2$ corresponds to the 12th observation $\therefore Q_2 = 2$

$\frac{3}{4}(23)$ $= 17.25 \Rightarrow Q_3$ corresponds to the 18th observation $\therefore Q_3 = 3$

To estimate the quartiles of a grouped frequency distribution the method of interpolation used to obtain the median is again used, but in this case using $\frac{1}{4}n$ and $\frac{3}{4}n$. For the data on visits to the doctor the quartiles are estimated as follows:

$$\text{Lower quartile} = Q_1 = b + \frac{(\frac{1}{4}n - f)}{f_m} \times w$$

where f, f_m and w now refer to the class containing the lower quartile.

$\therefore$ $$Q_1 = 4.5 + \frac{(37.5 - 32)}{71} \times 5 = 4.89$$

Similarly $$Q_3 = 9.5 + \frac{(112.5 - 103)}{20} \times 5 = 11.88$$

Two other sets of quantiles which are often used are the **deciles** ($D_1, D_2, ..., D_9$) and the **percentiles** ($P_1, P_2, ..., P_{99}$) which divide the data into 10 and 100 equal parts respectively.

Evaluation of the deciles and percentiles from raw data or frequency data uses the same approach as for the quartiles with $\frac{1}{4}n$ being replaced by $\frac{1}{10}n$ and $\frac{1}{100}n$ respectively. Thus for the data relating to the number of children in the family the third decile, D_3 is the value corresponding to $\frac{3}{10}(23) = 6.9$, i.e. the 7th observation. Thus $D_3 = 1$.

Similarly the 89th percentile, P_{89}, corresponds to $\frac{89}{100}(23) = 20.47$, i.e. the 21st value. Thus $P_{89} = 4$.

For grouped frequency distributions the approach used is the same as for the median and quartiles. Thus for the data on visits to the doctor the 6th decile and 85th percentile are estimated as follows.

$$D_6 = 4.5 + \left(\frac{\frac{6}{10}(150) - 32}{71} \right) \times 5 = 8.58$$

$$P_{85} = 14.5 + \left(\frac{\frac{85}{100}(150) - 123}{14} \right) \times 5 = 16.11$$

Example 1

A group of 14 children were given a test in mathematics. Their marks out of 20 were as shown below:

8 18 10 14 18 11 13 16 13 14 13 17 15 8

Find: (a) the mode, (b) the median, (c) the upper quartile of these marks.

Re-arranging these data in ascending order of magnitude gives

8 8 10 11 13 13 13 14 14 15 16 17 18 18

(a) The mode is the value which occurs most frequently.

$$\therefore \qquad\qquad \text{Mode} = 13$$

(b) For the median:

$$\tfrac{1}{2}(n+1) = \tfrac{15}{2} = 7.5$$

Thus, using the seventh and eighth observations:

$$Q_2 = \tfrac{1}{2}(13+14) = 13.5$$

(c) For the upper quartile:

$$\tfrac{3}{4}n = \tfrac{3}{4}(14) = 10.5$$

Thus, using the 11th observation:

$$Q_3 = 16$$

Example 2

The following distribution shows the number of orders for groceries received each week in a particular year by a village shop.

Number of orders	18	19	20	21	22	23	24	25	26	27	28
Number of weeks	2	2	3	4	6	9	12	6	5	2	1

Find: (a) the mode, (b) the median and the quartiles, (c) the seventh decile.

Cumulative frequencies corresponding to the orders are:

2 4 7 11 17 26 38 44 49 51 52

(a) Mode = 24

(b) Since $n = 52$ then

$$\tfrac{1}{2}(n+1) = \tfrac{53}{2} = 26.5$$

Thus, you use the 26th and 27th observations:

$$\text{Median} = \tfrac{1}{2}(23+24) = 23.5$$

For Q_1:

$$\tfrac{1}{4}n = \tfrac{52}{4} = 13$$

Thus, you use the 13th and 14th observations:

$$Q_1 = \tfrac{1}{2}(22 + 22) = 22$$

For Q_3:

$$\tfrac{3}{4}n = 39$$

Thus, you use the 39th and 40th observations:

$$Q_3 = \tfrac{1}{2}(25 + 25) = 25$$

(c) For D_7:

$$\tfrac{7}{10}n = 36.4$$

Thus, you use the 37th observation:

$$D_7 = 24$$

Example 3

The lengths of a batch of 2000 rods were measured to the nearest centimetre. The measurements are summarised below.

Length (to nearest cm)	Number of rods	Cumulative number of rods
60–64	11	11
65–69	49	60
70–74	190	250
75–79	488	738
80–84	632	1370
85–89	470	1840
90–94	137	1977
95–99	23	2000
Total	2000	

Estimate: (a) the median and the quartiles, (b) the third decile, (c) the sixty-seventh percentile.

(a)

$$Q_2 = 79.5 + \left(\frac{\tfrac{1}{2}(2000) - 738}{632}\right) \times 5 = 81.57$$

$$Q_1 = 74.5 + \left(\frac{\tfrac{1}{4}(2000) - 250}{488}\right) \times 5 = 77.06$$

$$Q_3 = 84.5 + \left(\frac{\tfrac{3}{4}(2000) - 1370}{470}\right) \times 5 = 85.88$$

(b)
$$D_3 = 74.5 + \left(\frac{\frac{3}{10}(2000) - 250}{488} \right) \times 5 = 78.09$$

(c)
$$P_{67} = 79.5 + \left(\frac{\frac{67}{100}(2000) - 738}{632} \right) \times 5 = 84.26$$

Stem and leaf diagrams

Although stem and leaf diagrams were only used in section 2.4 of chapter 2 to summarise data, they can in fact be used to find quantiles, in particular the quartiles.

Consider the stem and leaf diagram for example 3 on page 11.

Repair times			2	1 means 21
3	2	1 4 4		(3)
20	3	0 0 0 0 1 1 1 1 2 2 3 3 4 4 4 4 4		(17)
(8)	3	6 6 6 6 7 7 8 9		(8)
23	4	0 0 1 1 1 2 2 2 3 3		(10)
13	4	5 6 6 6 7		(5)
8	5	0 1 1 5 6 6		(6)
2	6	2 2		(2)

Notice that an additional column of information has been added to the left of the diagram. This is known as the **depth** column. The depth of a line indicates the number of leaves on that line or beyond it. The 20 on the second line down indicates that there are 20 leaves on that line or above it; the 13 on the third line from the bottom indicates that there are 13 leaves on that line or below it. The line with (8) on it contains the median and there are eight leaves on that line. To find the values of the quartiles from a stem and leaf diagram you use the same methods as before, counting the leaves from the top or bottom of the diagram until the appropriate values have been located. Thus for these data, proceed as follows.

For Q_1:
$$\tfrac{1}{4}n = \tfrac{51}{4} = 12.75 \Rightarrow 13\text{th observation}$$
$$\therefore \qquad\qquad Q_1 = 32$$

For Q_2:
$$\tfrac{1}{2}(n+1) = 26 \Rightarrow 26\text{th observation}$$
$$\therefore \qquad\qquad Q_2 = 37$$

For Q_3:
$$\tfrac{3}{4}n = 38.25 \Rightarrow 39\text{th observation}$$
$$\therefore \qquad\qquad Q_3 = 45$$

Deciles and percentiles can be found similarly as before.

Box plots

Now that you are familiar with quantiles and quartiles, it is possible to introduce another useful graphical method for representing data. This is known as a **box and whisker plot** or more commonly a **box plot**. The box is used to represent the central 50% of the data, and the whiskers which extend from the box to the smallest and largest values give an indication of the overall spread of the data, as shown below:

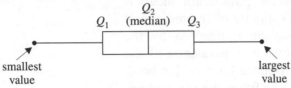

At this stage the box plot will be used simply as a means of representation. Later in this chapter its interpretation and use for comparisons will be considered. For the data on repair times it was found that $Q_1 = 32$, $Q_2 = 37$ and $Q_3 = 45$. The stem and leaf diagram shows that the smallest value is 21 and the largest value is 62. The box plot to represent these values is shown below:

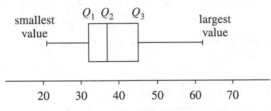

Questions involving the drawing of simple box plots like the one above will not be set on S1. Questions involving the interpretation of a given box plot can be set.

3.5 The mean

The third measure used to represent a data set is the arithmetic mean. You may be familiar with this measure from earlier studies and you may even use another name for it. The arithmetic mean is often referred to as the *average*, but from now on this measure will be referred to simply as the **mean** and defined as follows.

■ **The MEAN is the sum of all the observations divided by the total number of observations.**

Let us consider the height of three students chosen at random from year 13 in a sixth form college. The students are John, Sandra and Tony and their heights in inches are 70 in, 64 in and 73 in respectively. In statistical language the heights of John, Sandra and Tony are a **sample** of the heights of the **population** of year 13 students in the college. A population is a collection of individual items or individuals from which samples are drawn in order to make inferences about that population. In practice populations are usually too large to be handled numerically and so samples are taken from them and these samples are used to represent the population. Thus rather than find the mean of a population you take a sample from the population, evaluate its mean and use it as an estimate of the mean of the population. However, it is important to remember that the population will have a mean value even if you are unable to evaluate it. The value of the population mean is denoted by the Greek symbol μ and any estimate of the mean you evaluate from a sample from the population is denoted by the symbol $\bar{x}$. The population mean, μ is known as a **parameter** of the population. Other parameters will be introduced later in this book and in other books in the series. Consider the following illustration:

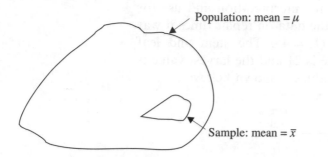

Since $\bar{x}$ is calculated from a sample in order to be able to make inferences about μ then it is essential that $\bar{x}$ is the *best representative value* of μ that can be obtained. In statistics, this best representative value is referred to as an *unbiased estimate* and although the proof is beyond the scope of this book it can be shown that the mean, $\bar{x}$, as defined earlier, is an unbiased estimate of μ. This implies that you can use the same method of evaluating the mean for both the population and a sample from that population. As will be seen later in this chapter it is not always the case that you can evaluate the population parameter and its estimate from a sample using the same method.

Consider the data on page 29 showing the errors made by each of 11 secretarial students:

$$4 \quad 6 \quad 7 \quad 5 \quad 9 \quad 10 \quad 6 \quad 6 \quad 4 \quad 7 \quad 8$$

Within the college at which these students are studying they may be the only secretarial students and they will then constitute the **population** of secretarial students at that college. For this population of students, the mean number of errors made is

$$\mu = \frac{4 + 6 + 7 + 5 + 9 + 10 + 6 + 6 + 4 + 7 + 8}{11} = \frac{72}{11} = 6.545$$

Rather than write out the sum of all the observations for each calculation as above you can introduce the $\sum$ notation where $\sum$ implies the sum of all the observations. Thus if you have a set of n observations, $x_1, x_2, ..., x_n$, from a population then the mean of this population of observations is given by:

$$\mu = \frac{\sum_{i=1}^{n} x_i}{n}$$

If you were to take a **sample** of 4 students from the above population and they made 7, 9, 6, 4 errors respectively then the mean of this sample is given by:

$$\bar{x} = \frac{\sum x}{n}$$

$$= \frac{26}{4} = 6.5$$

Note that the $i = 1$ and n have been removed from $\sum$ for simplicity since we can only sum the observations available in the population or sample.

In the case of a frequency distribution you need to extend the above notation, since each value of the variable has a frequency associated with it. Thus $x_1, x_2, ..., x_n$ have corresponding frequencies $f_1, f_2, ..., f_n$ implying that x_1 occurred f_1 times, etc. In this case the mean is found using:

$$\mu = \bar{x} = \frac{\sum fx}{\sum f}$$

Thus for the data relating to the sample of 23 families introduced earlier in this chapter the mean number of children per family is given by:

$$\bar{x} = \frac{(2 \times 0) + (5 \times 1) + (9 \times 2) + (4 \times 3) + (2 \times 4) + (1 \times 5)}{2 + 5 + 9 + 4 + 2 + 1}$$

$$= \frac{48}{23} = 2.09$$

Another 'health warning' is appropriate here! It is not unusual for students to give their answer as $\bar{x} = \frac{48}{6} = 8$ for this distribution, where the 6 comes from 0, 1, 2, 3, 4, 5, i.e. 6 values of the variable. First, it is totally wrong and second, it does not make sense. None of the families had 8 children, so 8 cannot possibly be a representative value for all 23 families. **Always check that your answer makes sense!**

The last calculation is often made easier using a simple table as shown below.

Number of children, x	Number of families, f	f × x
0	2	0
1	5	5
2	9	18
3	4	12
4	2	8
5	1	5
Total	23	48

Hence:

$$\bar{x} = \frac{\sum fx}{\sum f}$$

$$= \frac{48}{23}$$

$$= 2.09$$

For raw data and data summarised by means of a frequency distribution the variable values, x_1, x_2, ..., x_n, are very obvious. This is *not* the case when data are summarised in a grouped frequency distribution. For example, what are the x_1, x_2, etc. for the data on page 30 relating to the visits to the doctor? In Chapter 2 the term **class mid-point** was introduced. The class mid-point can be used to represent the class since you have no information as to how data is distributed within a class.

Thus for the class 0–4, use $\frac{1}{2}(0+4) = 2$ as the class mid-point and this becomes x_1 with a corresponding frequency of 32 associated with it. Once the mid-points of all the classes have been found you can then proceed as for a frequency distribution using the mid-points as x_1, x_2, ..., x_n. The calculation is easily carried out using a simple table as shown below:

Visits	Frequency, f	Class mid-point, x	f × x
0–4	32	2	64
5–9	71	7	497
10–14	20	12	240
15–19	14	17	238
20–24	10	22	220
25–29	3	27	81
Total	150		1340

Hence:

$$\bar{x} = \frac{\sum fx}{\sum f}$$
$$= \frac{1340}{150}$$
$$= 8.93$$

At this point it is worth pausing to think about any advantages and disadvantages associated with the mean. There are two disadvantages to consider.

First, the mean is influenced by extreme values. If you have five observations as follows: 3, 4, 5, 6, 7, then the mean is found to be:

$$\bar{x} = \frac{3 + 4 + 5 + 6 + 7}{5}$$
$$= \frac{25}{5}$$
$$= 5$$

If the next observation is an extreme one, say 35, then

$$\bar{x} = \frac{25 + 35}{6}$$
$$= \frac{60}{6}$$
$$= 10$$

Thus it can be seen that the mean has been drawn towards the extreme value.

Second, and in this age of calculators perhaps not too big a disadvantage, the mean is not as easily calculated as the two earlier measures.

The advantages, however, tend to outweigh the disadvantages, the first being that all the values are used directly when calculating the mean. The second, and more important one, is that the mean has very important mathematical properties, which at this stage may not be obvious or seem important. Their importance should become clear in chapter 9.

There are times when it is desirable to combine data sets and in such situations the mean of the combined data set can be obtained from the means of the individual data sets. This is done by weighting the mean of each data set according to the number of observations in each data set. For example, if the mean of a sample of 25 observations is 8.75 and the mean of a different sample of 30 observations is 9.28 then the mean of the combined sample is given by:

$$\bar{x} = \frac{(25 \times 8.75) + (30 \times 9.28)}{25 + 30}$$
$$= \frac{497.15}{55}$$
$$= 9.04$$

Example 4

Over a period of 10 days a commuter timed, to the nearest minute, how long it took her to travel from home to her work. The following are her observations.

$$35 \quad 27 \quad 38 \quad 26 \quad 31 \quad 42 \quad 32 \quad 29 \quad 38 \quad 34$$

(a) Find the mean length of time it took her to travel to work.

At a later date she carried out the same process over a period of 15 days and found her mean time to be 36.4 minutes.

(b) Find the mean time for the combined sample of 25 observations.

(a)
$$\bar{x} = \frac{\sum x}{\sum n}$$
$$= \frac{35 + 27 + \ldots + 34}{10}$$
$$= \frac{332}{10}$$
$$= 33.2 \text{ minutes}$$

(b)
$$\bar{x} = \frac{n_1 x_1 + n_2 x_2}{n_1 + n_2}$$
$$= \frac{332 + (15 \times 36.4)}{10 + 15}$$
$$= \frac{878}{25}$$
$$= 35.12 \text{ minutes}$$

Example 5

A car park attendant counted the number of people in each car entering a car park between 7.30 am and 9.00 am and his results are summarised in the following frequency distribution:

Number of people	1	2	3	4	5
Number of cars	41	33	18	6	2

Calculate the mean number of people per car entering the car park.

Number of people, x	Number of cars, f	$f \times x$
1	41	41
2	33	66
3	18	54
4	6	24
5	2	10
Total	100	195

$$\text{Mean} = \bar{x} = \frac{\sum fx}{\sum f}$$

$$= \frac{195}{100}$$

$$= 1.95$$

Example 6

From a spot check of the speeds of vehicles on a motorway, the following grouped frequency distribution was obtained:

Speed (m.p.h.)	56–58	59–61	62–64	65–67	68–70	71–73	74–76
Number of vehicles	4	12	28	58	44	18	10

Find the average speed of the vehicles involved on this spot check.

Speed (m.p.h.)	Number of vehicles, f	Mid-point, x	fx
56–58	4	57	228
59–61	12	60	720
62–64	28	63	1764
65–67	58	66	3828
68–70	44	69	3036
71–73	18	72	1296
74–76	10	75	750
Total	174		11622

$$\therefore \qquad \bar{x} = \frac{\sum fx}{\sum f}$$

$$= \frac{11622}{174}$$

$$= 66.79 \text{ m.p.h.}$$

You will no doubt have noticed that the arithmetic in Example 6 involved quite large numbers and whilst these are no problem with a modern calculator it is worth at this point giving some consideration to the reduction of this involved arithmetic. In statistics this is done using **coding**, whereby the original variable is transformed to a simpler one which eases the arithmetic. For example, if you wish to find the mean of the five observations 1001, 1002, 1003, 1004, 1005 then you could use:

$$\bar{x} = \frac{1001 + 1002 + 1003 + 1004 + 1005}{5}$$

$$= \frac{1015}{5}$$

$$= 1003$$

Alternatively, if you subtract 1000 from each observation you obtain the values 1, 2, 3, 4, 5 and the mean of these five values is 3. If you now add the 1000 which was originally subtracted then the value obtained is 1003, as before.

Consider the observations 1010, 1020, 1030, 1040, 1050. If you subtract 1000 from each of these observations you obtain the values 10, 20, 30, 40, 50. Dividing each value by 10 gives the values 1, 2, 3, 4, 5 and you already know that the mean of these values is 3. If you now multiply by 10 and add on 1000 the mean of the original observations is $(3 \times 10) + 1000 = 1030$. In general, if you have n observations x_1, x_2, ..., x_n and each observation is transformed or **coded** such that

$$y_1 = (x_1 - a)/b, \ y_2 = (x_2 - a)/b, \ ..., \ y_n = (x_n - a)/b,$$

(i.e. subtract a then divide by b) then $\bar{x} = b\bar{y} + a$.

The effect of this coding is illustrated graphically below.

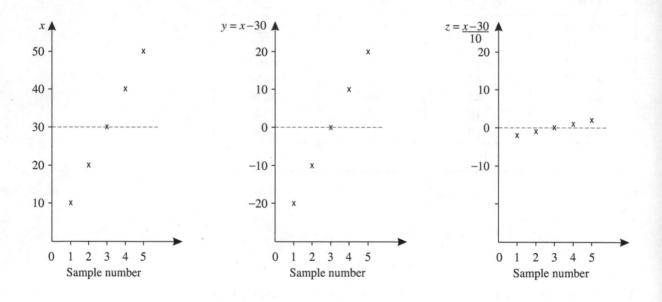

As can be seen the effect of subtracting a constant (i.e. $y = x - 30$) is the equivalent of moving the origin without affecting the spread of the data. The effect of dividing by a constant has the effect of reducing the spread of the data about this line of origin. This illustration may prove useful later in this chapter. In a practical situation it is necessary to choose suitable values for a and b in order to code the data using $y = (x - a)/b$. A simple rule-of-thumb is to let a take the x value corresponding to the modal frequency and to let b equal the class width. If the class widths are not all equal then use the smallest class width.

Example 7

Use the method of coding to estimate the mean of the grouped frequency distribution in example 6.

In this case, let $a = 66$ and $b = 3$, then, for example, when $x = 57$,
$y = \dfrac{x - 66}{3}$ gives $y = -3$.

The following table illustrates the way to carry out the calculation.

Speed (m.p.h.)	Number of vehicles, f	Mid-point, x	$y = \dfrac{x - 66}{3}$	fy
56–58	4	57	−3	−12
59–61	12	60	−2	−24
62–64	28	63	−1	−28
65–67	58	66	0	0
68–70	44	69	1	44
71–73	18	72	2	36
74–76	10	75	3	30
Total	174			−64 + 110 = 46

$\therefore \qquad \bar{y} = \dfrac{\sum fy}{\sum f}$

$\qquad\qquad = \dfrac{46}{174}$

$\therefore \qquad \bar{x} = b\bar{y} + a$

$\qquad\qquad = 3 \times \dfrac{46}{174} + 66$

$\qquad\qquad = 66.79 \text{ m.p.h.}$

Note the simplification of the arithmetic – the only need for a calculator is to evaluate $\dfrac{46}{174}$, the rest is simple mental arithmetic. At this point it is worth issuing another 'health warning' relating to showing your working when answering examination questions. Entering numbers into your calculator, pressing the appropriate keys and writing down an answer scores full marks if the answer is *completely correct* to the required number of decimal places. The slightest error results in a score of zero marks. Showing your working at all stages will gain the method marks available and marks for accuracy will be lost at the stage the error is made – subsequent accuracy marks may well be awarded. For example if −24 above had appeared as −26 and thus

$$\bar{y} = \tfrac{44}{174} \Rightarrow \bar{x} = 66.76$$

then it is quite likely that all but one of the available marks would have been gained. An answer of 66.76 without working would have scored zero marks.

Before leaving this section it is necessary to consider two additional features associated with grouped frequency distributions. The first concerns *unequal class intervals*. In some circumstances data are grouped to reflect the uneven spread of the data being grouped. For example, if most of the data are in the range 0–50, but some lie in the range 50–250 then the classes used might be 0–9, 10–19, 20–29, 30–49, 50–74, 75–99, 100–149, 150–249. Unequal class widths such as these were easily dealt with when drawing histograms and they should not cause any problems when estimating the median or the mean since the same methods can be used with distributions with unequal intervals as are used with distributions with equal intervals.

The second feature relates to *open-ended classes*. These are classes appearing at the beginning or end of a distribution such that they do not have either a lower limit or an upper limit. For example, –9, 10–19, ..., 80–89, 90–. The first class implies any value less than or equal to 9 and the last class implies any value greater than or equal to 90. Although open-ended classes do not affect the estimation of the median, they do affect the drawing of histograms and the estimation of the mean. They are used when there is uncertainty about the least value or maximum value that could occur in a distribution and if an estimate for the mean of that distribution is required then the open-ended classes need to be closed. To do this needs a rule-of-thumb and the common one is to use 'twice the previous class interval'.

Thus for the class 90– you could use 90–109 since the interval of the class 80–89 is 10 (i.e. 89.5–79.5) and for 90–109 it is 20. It is not essential to use this rule-of-thumb since it may not always be appropriate. There are instances when you will know intuitively what value to use and this is perfectly acceptable. It is advisable that at some point you explain why you have used this value. For example, with –9 it may be that 0–9 is appropriate since you know that the variable cannot be negative.

Exercise 3A

1 For each of the sets of data given below find or estimate, as appropriate, the mode (or modal class) and the median.

(a) 4 10 15 8 3 8 9 7 6

(b)

Number	10	11	12	13	14	15
Frequency	4	6	13	18	7	5

(c)

Class	0–4	5–9	10–14	15–19	20–24	25–30
Frequency	2	6	7	9	8	4

2 For each of the sets of data given below find or estimate, as appropriate, the quartiles.

(a) 3   8   8   2   2   7   9   10   7

(b)

Number	0	1	2	3	4	5	6	7	8	9	10
Frequency	1	1	4	8	12	14	7	6	4	2	1

(c)

Class	1–9	10–19	20–29	30–39	40–49	50–59	60–69
Frequency	3	6	12	18	10	4	2

3 For each of the sets of data given below find or estimate, as appropriate, D_3 and D_9.

(a) 19   22   30   14   26   37   42   32   33   10

(b)

Number	10–12	13–15	16–18	19–21	22–24	25–27
Frequency	3	9	14	23	26	9

(c)

Number	0	1	2	3	4	5	6	7	8
Frequency	2	3	4	4	5	3	2	1	1

4 For each of the sets of data given below find or estimate, as appropriate, P_{33} and P_{66}.

(a) 33   42   45   48   50   57   60   75   80   83

(b)

Number	10	11	12	13	14	15	16	17	18
Frequency	4	14	24	42	36	21	14	3	2

(c)

Class	11–20	21–30	31–40	41–50	51–60	61–70	71–80
Frequency	8	12	15	16	11	6	2

5 At a garage which did MOT car tests, the number of cars tested each day, over a 13 day working period, was as follows.

3   10   8   6   8   3   2   2   8   7   11   12   4

Find: (a) the mode, (b) the median, (c) the lower quartile, of these numbers.

6 Below is the frequency distribution which resulted when the height (in cm) of 50 tennis players was measured.

Height (cm)	170	172.5	175	177.5	180	182.5	185	187.5	190	192.5	195
Frequency	1	2	4	6	8	9	7	6	3	2	2

Find: (a) the mode, (b) the median and quartiles, (c) the third decile, of these data.

7 When checking the number of weeds growing in a field by using a 1 metre by 1 metre sampling frame, the frequency distribution was as summarised below.

Weeds per square metre	0	1	2	3	4	5	6	7	8
Frequency	4	15	27	20	18	10	4	1	1

Find: (a) the mode, (b) the median, (c) the upper quartile and the eighth decile, for these data.

8 The grouped frequency distribution shown below gives the speed of service of the top 50 performers in men's professional tennis in 1992.

Service speed (m.p.h.)	90–94	95–99	100–104	105–109	110–114	115–119	120–124	125–129
Frequency	2	7	9	14	9	4	3	2

Estimate: (a) the median and lower quartile, (b) the third and seventh deciles, (c) the thirty-ninth percentile, of these data.

9 Use the stem and leaf diagram given below to find the median and the quartiles of these data:

```
                        1 | 1 means 11

          1 | 1 5              (2)
          2 | 2 4 6 6          (4)
          3 | 2 5 6 7 7        (5)
          4 | 0 0 1 4 6 8 8    (7)
          5 | 0 1 1 5          (4)
          6 | 2 4 4 7          (4)
          7 | 8                (1)
          8 | 2 2              (2)
```

10 When analysing the lengths of sentences, the number of words per sentence in one paragraph were:

      29 14 15 27 30 33 10 20 20 21

(a) Find the mean number of words per sentence.

(b) In another passage of the same book, over 16 sentences, the mean was found to be 35.2 words per sentence. Find the mean for the two passages combined.

11 A car dealer sells three different models made by the same manufacturer. He sells

265 of model A at a mean price of £10 860,

352 of model B at a mean price of £12 580

150 of model C at a mean price of £18 250.

Find the mean price of all the cars sold during this period.

12 The number of general knowledge questions answered correctly during a test taken by 100 children is shown in the following frequency distribution:

Number of correct answers	1	2	3	4	5	6
Frequency	11	18	26	23	15	7

Calculate the mean number of correct answers.

13 The frequency distribution of the number of peas in a pod, for a sample of 90 pods, taken at random, from a new variety of pea is shown below.

Number of peas per pod	2	3	4	5	6	7	8
Frequency	5	8	10	11	19	27	10

Find the mean number of peas per pod for this sample.

14 For a selected group of people, an insurance company gave the following data:

Age	0–9	10–19	20–29	30–39	40–49	50–59	60–69	70–79
Number of deaths	2	12	55	95	71	42	16	7

Estimate the mean age of death.

15 The grouped frequency distribution for the life (in hours) of
200 electric light bulbs is given below.

Life (hours)	590–599	600–609	610–619	620–629	630–639	640–649	650–659	660–669
Frequency	4	9	23	41	81	29	9	4

Use a method of coding to estimate the mean life expectancy
of a light bulb in this sample.

SUMMARY OF KEY POINTS

1 The **mode** is that value of a variable which occurs most
   frequently.

2 The **median** is the middle value of an ordered set of data.

3 The **quartiles** of an ordered set of data are such that 25%
   of the observations are less than or equal to the first
   quartile (Q_1), 50% are less than or equal to the second
   quartile (Q_2) and 75% are less than or equal to the third
   quartile (Q_3).

4 The **mean** of a set of observations is the sum of all the
   observations divided by the total number of observations,
   i.e.

$$\mu = \bar{x} = \frac{\sum x}{n} \qquad \text{or} \qquad \frac{\sum fx}{\sum f}$$

Methods for summarising data (dispersion)

4

4.1 Measures of dispersion

So far this book has been concerned with calculating or estimating a single value to represent a set of data, for example, the mode, the median or the mean. The outcome has usually been a single value, such as the mean is equal to 12.72, although for grouped frequency data the modal class was quoted rather than a single value. This idea of using a range of values (for example, modal class is 20–24) can now be expanded upon since it is essential that you realise that although you can quote a single number to represent data, the data itself will be spread about that number. It is this measuring of the spread of data that will now be considered.

4.2 Range and interquartile range

The simplest measure that quantifies the spread of a data set is the **range** which is easily and simply defined as follows.

■ **The RANGE of a set of data is the value obtained when the smallest value is subtracted from the largest value.**

Example 1
Find the range of the following observations giving the number of absentees from the statistics class of 40 students over a period of ten days:

$$3 \quad 8 \quad 7 \quad 1 \quad 2 \quad 9 \quad 8 \quad 2 \quad 4 \quad 5$$

$$\text{Range} = \text{largest value} - \text{smallest value}$$
$$= 9 - 1$$
$$= 8$$

Although the range is easily calculated it does not lend itself to mathematical use and thus it tends to be used only with small data sets in conjunction with either the mode or the median.

This concept of range can be extended to the quantiles and in particular to the quartiles, giving the following definitions.

■ **The INTERQUARTILE RANGE (IQR) is the value obtained when the lower quartile is subtracted from the upper quartile.**

$$IQR = Q_3 - Q_1$$

In some situations the **semi-interquartile range (SIQR)** is used where

$$SIQR = \tfrac{1}{2}(Q_3 - Q_1)$$

Example 2

For the data in example 1, find the upper and lower quartiles and hence the semi-interquartile range.

Re-arranging the data in ascending order of magnitude gives:

$$1 \quad 2 \quad 2 \quad 3 \quad 4 \quad 5 \quad 7 \quad 8 \quad 8 \quad 9$$

For Q_1: $\quad\quad \tfrac{1}{4}n = \tfrac{10}{4} = 2.5 \Rightarrow$ 3rd observation

$\therefore \quad\quad\quad\quad\quad\quad\quad\quad\quad Q_1 = 2$

For Q_3: $\quad\quad \tfrac{3}{4}n = 7.5 \Rightarrow$ 8th observation

$\therefore \quad\quad\quad\quad\quad\quad\quad\quad\quad Q_3 = 8$

$$\therefore \quad\quad SIQR = \tfrac{1}{2}(Q_3 - Q_1)$$
$$= \tfrac{1}{2}(8 - 2)$$
$$= 3$$

The calculations are relatively easy but the IQR and SIQR do not lend themselves to easy mathematical use. They are based on the central 50% of the data and are thus not influenced by extreme values and are often used when data contains extreme values, or has open-ended classes or is not symmetrical. This property of symmetry will be discussed in section 4.3. In these situations it is not unusual to use the median and the SIQR (or IQR) to summarise a data set.

Whilst the IQR does not lend itself to easy mathematical use, it can be used in conjunction with a box plot. Sometimes a set of data will contain one or more extreme values, known as **outliers**. These are values which do not fit into the main body of the data and when such values occur they need to be highlighted. This can be done when representing the data by a box plot. In chapter 3 the box plots were assumed not to have any outliers but in this section data which contain outliers will be considered. As in other areas of statistics it is necessary to be aware that there are no fixed rules when drawing box plots with outliers. In this book the rule adopted will be based on one and a half times interquartile range $- 1.5(Q_3 - Q_1)$. Thus to construct a box plot proceed as follows:

> The range and IQR will not be the direct focus of questions on the S1 examination paper. They may be used to draw simple inferences or to help with interpretation of data.

1 Find the values of the quartiles: Q_1, Q_2 and Q_3.
2 Evaluate $Q_1 - 1.5(Q_3 - Q_1)$ and $Q_3 + 1.5(Q_3 - Q_1)$ and note any values less than $Q_1 - 1.5(Q_3 - Q_1)$ and greater than $Q_3 + 1.5(Q_3 - Q_1)$. These values are the outliers.

3 Draw a box based on the values Q_1, Q_2, Q_3 as in chapter 3. If there are no values less than $Q_1 - 1.5(Q_3 - Q_1)$ the left-hand whisker can be drawn to stop at the lowest value in the data. If there are one or more outliers with values less than $Q_1 - 1.5(Q_3 - Q_1)$ then the left-hand whisker is drawn from Q_1 and stops at $Q_1 - 1.5(Q_3 - Q_1)$. The individual outliers are then marked with crosses ($\times$).

4 The right-hand whisker is drawn similarly but using $Q_3 + 1.5(Q_3 - Q_1)$. Thus this whisker stops at the largest value of the data if it is less than $Q_3 + 1.5(Q_3 - Q_1)$ or at $Q_3 + 1.5(Q_3 - Q_1)$. Points beyond that are marked individually.

5 An alternative method of plotting is to stop the whisker at the first value that is not an outlier.

Example 3

Consider the data in example 1 relating to the number of absentees from a statistics class. If on an eleventh day 19 students had been absent than the ordered data would be:

$$1 \quad 2 \quad 2 \quad 3 \quad 4 \quad 5 \quad 7 \quad 8 \quad 8 \quad 9 \quad 19$$

In this case $Q_1 = 2$, $Q_2 = 5$, $Q_3 = 8$,

$$Q_1 - 1.5(Q_3 - Q_1) = -7 \quad \text{and} \quad Q_3 + 1.5(Q_3 - Q_1) = 17$$

There is one outlier with a value of 19.

The box plot would then be drawn as follows:

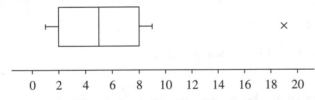

This example uses the method described in 5 above.

Example 4

Data were collected such that $Q_1 = 42$, $Q_2 = 47$ and $Q_3 = 50$. For these data $Q_1 - 1.5(Q_3 - Q_1) = 42 - 1.5(50 - 42) = 30$, $Q_3 + 1.5(Q_3 - Q_1) = 50 + 1.5(50 - 42) = 62$.

There were 3 outliers with values of 25, 65 and 67. In this case the box plot would be drawn as follows:

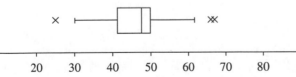

This example uses the method described in 3 and 4 above. Either method is acceptable for questions on the S1 paper.

As mentioned earlier, there are no fixed rules for drawing such box plots. Some texts use $Q_1 - 1.0$ IQR or $Q_1 - 2.0$ IQR but if data in the S1 paper contain outliers the method of identifying them will be given.

4.3 Variance and standard deviation

The fact that in the previous section reference was made to the lack of mathematical properties of the range and inter-quartile range suggests that there is a measure of spread or dispersion which does have suitable mathematical properties. This measure is known as the **standard deviation**. This section is concerned solely with its calculation or estimation. Its usefulness, through its mathematical properties, will be considered in Book S2. The one measure of location, previously considered, that is useful mathematically is the mean, and evaluation of the variance of a set of data is based on the mean of that data; μ for a population or $\bar{x}$ for a sample. Rather than use the range of a data set you can consider the deviations of a set of observations about their mean. Since the mean is the representative value of the data and is a *focus* for the data, then it is only to be expected that some of the observations will be smaller than the mean and some will be larger.

Consider a **population** consisting of the following values:

$$2 \quad 3 \quad 7 \quad 4 \quad 9$$

The mean, μ, is 5 and the individual deviations of the observations from the mean are:

$$-3 \quad -2 \quad 2 \quad -1 \quad 4$$

Note that the sum of these deviations is zero. This is always true, as is shown below.

Let x_1, x_2, ..., x_n represent a population of n observations and μ the mean of the population. The deviations from the mean are then

$$(x_1 - \mu), (x_2 - \mu), ..., (x_n - \mu).$$

The sum of these deviations is given by

$$\sum (x - \mu) = \sum x - \sum \mu$$
$$= \sum x - n\mu$$
$$= \sum x - n\frac{\sum x}{n}$$
$$= 0$$

To overcome this situation the variance is based on the sum of the deviations squared, a fact which may be difficult to understand at this stage. Thus we use $(x_1 - \mu)^2$, ..., $(x_n - \mu)^2$. Another very difficult feature associated with variance needs to be introduced at this point and whilst some attempt will be made to justify this feature, it will be necessary to wait until Book S3 before a proof can be given. Having obtained the squared deviations, the variance of a population is based on the sum of these squared deviations. Since you are dealing with a population then a Greek symbol, σ^2, is used to denote the population variance and its definition is then as follows:

- **The VARIANCE of a population of observations x_1, x_2, ..., x_n is the mean of the sum of the squared deviations from their mean, μ.**

i.e.
$$\sigma^2 = \frac{\sum(x - \mu)^2}{n}$$

For a population summarised by a frequency distribution the definition reflects the fact that each observation has a corresponding frequency and thus in this situation

$$\sigma^2 = \frac{\sum f(x - \mu)^2}{\sum f}$$

For a grouped frequency distribution the same definition is used but it must be remembered that the mid-points of the classes are used as the x-values in the calculation.

Whilst the above formulae define the variance, in practice it is usual to use a more computationally-friendly form for the variance. Thus it can be shown that:

$$\sigma^2 = \frac{\sum(x - \mu)^2}{n}$$

$$= \frac{\sum x^2}{n} - \mu^2$$

or
$$\sigma^2 = \frac{\sum f(x - \mu)^2}{\sum f}$$

$$= \frac{\sum fx^2}{\sum f} - \mu^2$$

Having defined variance in this way it is important to note that it is measured in terms of x^2 and not x. Thus, whatever the units of x, the variance is measured in (units)^2. To overcome the difficulty of interpreting a measure of spread expressed in (units)^2 a measure is used called the **standard deviation**. This is a measure of spread or variability which has the same units as the original observations and is defined as follows:

- **The STANDARD DEVIATION is the positive square root of the variance.**

Thus
$$\sigma = \sqrt{\frac{\sum(x - \mu)^2}{n}}$$

$$= \sqrt{\frac{\sum x^2}{n} - \mu^2}$$

or
$$\sigma = \sqrt{\frac{\sum f(x - \mu)^2}{\sum f}}$$

$$= \sqrt{\frac{\sum fx^2}{\sum f} - \mu^2}$$

Both variance and standard deviation are measures which you might find difficult to come to terms with after such simple measures as, for example, the mode or the mean. However, it is important that you understand how to evaluate them in order to use them in chapter 9, where the link between μ and σ^2 will be made.

Example 5

Consider the **population** of values defined earlier on page 56:

$$2 \quad 3 \quad 7 \quad 4 \quad 9$$

Find the mean and the variance of this population.

$$\mu = \frac{\sum x}{n}$$

$$= \frac{25}{5}$$

$$= 5$$

x	$(x - \mu)$	$(x - \mu)^2$	x^2
2	-3	9	4
3	-2	4	9
7	2	4	49
4	-1	1	16
9	4	16	81
25		34	159

$\therefore$
$$\sigma^2 = \frac{\sum(x - \mu)^2}{n}$$

$$= \frac{34}{5}$$

$$= 6.8$$

or
$$\sigma^2 = \frac{\sum x^2}{n} - \mu^2$$

$$= \tfrac{159}{5} - (5)^2$$

$$= 6.8$$

Using $\sum (x - \mu)^2$ is not recommended since in most situations μ is not an integer and thus rounding errors are introduced.

Example 6
Each member of an athletics club was asked to monitor the distance run in training during a particular week. The table below summarises the results. Estimate the mean and the standard deviation of this *population* of athletes.

Distance (to nearest km)	Number of athletes, f	Mid-point, x	fx	fx^2
31–40	10	35.5	355	12602.5
41–45	15	43	645	27735
46–50	20	48	960	46080
51–55	70	53	3710	196630
56–57	64	56.5	3616	204304
58–60	24	59	1416	83544
61–70	20	65.5	1310	85805
71–90	10	80.5	805	64802.5
	233		12817	721503

$$\mu = \tfrac{12817}{233} = 55.009 \qquad \sigma^2 = \tfrac{721503}{233} - \left(\tfrac{12817}{233}\right)^2 = 70.6351$$

$$\therefore \qquad \sigma = 8.404$$

You will have noticed that so far within this section much emphasis has been placed on *population data*. In practice, however, most data is sample data and you need to know how to estimate the variance of a population using sample data. It is the population that is of interest, not the sample. In the section on the mean on page 40 it was stated that $\bar{x}$, the sample mean, was the best (i.e. unbiased) estimator of μ the population mean and you could evaluate both μ and $\bar{x}$ using $\frac{\sum x}{n}$. Unfortunately, to estimate the variance of a population using a sample it is not possible to use the same method as for a population, as the value of μ is not known. If μ is replaced by $\bar{x}$ in $\frac{\sum (x - \mu)^2}{n}$ then it can be shown that $\frac{\sum (x - \bar{x})^2}{n}$ is not the most accurate or best (unbiased) estimator of σ^2, the population variance. In the same way that the value of the population mean μ was estimated from a sample and was denoted by $\bar{x}$, so the value of σ^2, is estimated by s^2. To obtain the most accurate (or unbiased) estimate of σ^2, the population variance, use

$$s^2 = \frac{\sum(x - \bar{x})^2}{n - 1}$$

Note that μ has been replaced by $\bar{x}$ and the divisor n by $n - 1$. Since we do not know μ it does not seem unreasonable to replace it by $\bar{x}$, but why do we divide by $n - 1$ and not n? The mathematical proof is given in Book S3 but a simple explanation is as follows. Since, as was shown earlier, $\sum(x - \mu) = 0$ then so is $\sum(x - \bar{x})$ and this implies that if you know $(n - 1)$ of the $(x - \bar{x})$ values then you can easily obtain the other one since their sum is zero. This means that you are only free to choose $(n - 1)$ of the deviations before the other becomes fixed and thus we divide by $(n - 1)$ rather than n. Thus:

$$s^2 = \frac{\sum(x - \bar{x})^2}{n - 1}$$

$$= \frac{1}{n - 1}\left\{\sum x^2 - \frac{(\sum x)^2}{n}\right\}$$

and
$$s^2 = \frac{\sum f(x - \bar{x})^2}{\sum f - 1}$$

$$= \frac{1}{\sum f - 1}\left\{\sum fx^2 - \frac{(\sum fx)^2}{\sum f}\right\}$$

with the standard deviation, s, being the positive square root of s^2.

Example 7

The following table summarises the distance, to the nearest mile, travelled to work by a random sample of commuters.

Distance (miles)	Number of commuters
0–9	15
10–19	38
20–29	22
30–39	15
40–49	8
50–59	2
Total	100

Estimate the mean and the standard deviation of this distribution.

Distance	Number of commuters, f	Mid-point, x	$y = \dfrac{x - 14.5}{10}$	fy	fy^2
0–9	15	4.5	−1	−15	15
10–19	38	14.5	0	0	0
20–29	22	24.5	1	22	22
30–39	15	34.5	2	30	60
40–49	8	44.5	3	24	72
50–59	2	54.5	4	8	32
	100			$-15 + 84$ $= 69$	201

$$\therefore \quad \bar{y} = \frac{\sum fy}{\sum f}$$

$$= \tfrac{69}{100}$$

$$= 0.69$$

$$s_y^2 = \frac{1}{\sum f - 1} \left\{ \sum fy^2 - \frac{(\sum fy)^2}{\sum f} \right\}$$

$$= \tfrac{1}{99} \left\{ 201 - \tfrac{(69)^2}{100} \right\} = 1.5494$$

$$\therefore \quad s_y = \sqrt{1.5494}$$

$$= 1.24$$

You will have noticed that this example has been solved using coding, such that $y = (x - 14.5)/10$. You now need to reverse the effect of this coding in order to obtain answers in terms of the original data. Thus:

$$\bar{x} = 10\bar{y} + 14.5$$

$$= (10 \times 0.69) + 14.5 = 21.4$$

As you will remember from chapter 3, subtracting a constant from the data does not affect the spread of the data, but division by a constant does. Thus you can ignore the 14.5 when converting s_y to s_x but you must remember to multiply by 10.

Hence $\qquad\qquad s_x = 10s_y = 12.4$

Without coding:

$$\sum fx = 2140 \qquad \text{and} \qquad \sum fx^2 = 61135$$

$$\therefore \qquad \bar{x} = \tfrac{2140}{100} = 21.4$$

and $\qquad s_x^2 = \tfrac{1}{99} \left\{ 61135 - \tfrac{(2140)^2}{100} \right\} = 154.9394$

$$\therefore \qquad s_x = \sqrt{154.9394} = 12.4$$

4.4 Interpretation

Before leaving this chapter, it is worth giving some consideration to ways in which the measures of location and dispersion can be interpreted and used. Each of the measures has been defined and in most cases their definition can be thought of as part of their interpretation. For example, the mode is the most frequently occurring value, so that if you were considering buying shoes for a large shoe shop then knowing the modal shoe size would enable you to cater for many of the customers. People with very small feet or very large ones, would not be too pleased but in any distribution they would find themselves in the first or last (possibly open-ended) class. Similarly, the quartiles indicate that there is 50% of data between Q_1 and Q_3 and thus definition and interpretation are obviously linked.

Whilst the mean and standard deviation or the median and semi-interquartile range can be used to measure location and dispersion within a data set, they can also be used to measure dispersion between data sets. Consider the following data sets:

$$x: \quad 6 \quad 7 \quad 8 \quad 9 \quad 10 \quad 11 \quad 12$$
$$y: \quad 56 \quad 57 \quad 58 \quad 59 \quad 60 \quad 61 \quad 62$$

Treating these as *populations* you get:

$$\mu_x = 9 \qquad \sigma_x = 2$$
$$\mu_y = 59 \qquad \sigma_y = 2$$

and the percentage increase in x is:

$$\frac{12 - 6}{6} \times 100 = 100\%$$

and in y is:

$$\frac{62 - 56}{56} \times 100 = 10.7\%.$$

Thus x has a much greater percentage spread than y. To enable you to compare the **relative dispersion** between data sets, use the **coefficient of variation**, V, which is defined as:

$$V = \frac{100 \times \sigma}{\mu} \qquad \text{or} \qquad \frac{100 \times s}{\bar{x}}$$

For x, you get:

$$V = \frac{100 \times 2}{9} = 22.2\%$$

and for y:

$$V = \frac{100 \times 2}{59} = 3.4\%$$

Notice that V does not have units, but is a percentage and thus you can use it to make comparisons between data sets.

There are times however when the quartiles can be used to describe the *shape of a data set*. Consider the following three histograms representing three different distributions:

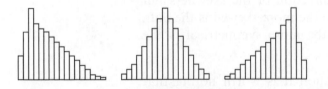

Each histogram has a different shape and a statistical name is given to each of them. The middle histogram has a line of symmetry through its central bar and hence it is known as a **symmetrical distribution**. One of the important facts about a symmetrical distribution is that the mode, median and mean are all equal. The other two distributions are not symmetrical and they are known as **skew distributions**. The one on the left is **positive skew** (the tail of the distribution extends in the direction of the positive axis) and the one on the right is **negative skew**. For relatively simple distributions, such as those represented by these histograms the following rules-of-thumb can be applied:

positive skew: mode < median < mean.
negative skew: mean < median < mode.

An alternative method of indicating skewness is to use the quartiles. If the median (Q_2) is closer to the lower quartile (Q_1) than it is to the upper quartile (Q_3) then the distribution is positive skew; if the median is equidistant from the lower quartile and the upper quartile the distribution is symmetrical; if the median is closer to Q_3 than it is to Q_1 then the distribution is negative skew. The above are easily seen on a box plot as illustrated by the box plots shown below.

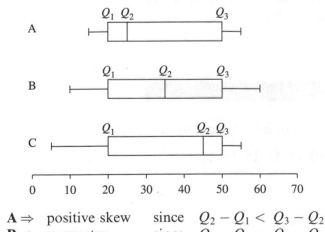

Thus: **A** $\Rightarrow$ positive skew   since $Q_2 - Q_1 < Q_3 - Q_2$
       B $\Rightarrow$ symmetry   since $Q_2 - Q_1 = Q_3 - Q_2$
       C $\Rightarrow$ negative skew since $Q_2 - Q_1 > Q_3 - Q_2$

A third method of assessing the skewness of a distribution is to evaluate:

$$\frac{3\,(\text{mean} - \text{median})}{\text{standard deviation}}$$

This method not only indicates the direction of the skewness but also quantifies it – the larger the value the more skewed is the data and the closer the value is to zero the more symmetrical is the distribution.

When data is skewed in either direction it is worth noting that rather than use the mean and standard deviation as appropriate measures of location and dispersion the median and semi-interquartile range are used, since as you will remember the mean is affected by extreme values and the median is not. Skew distributions tend to include extreme values. With this in mind we can measure relative dispersion by the **quartile coefficient of variation**, QV, where:

$$QV = \frac{100 \times \frac{1}{2}(Q_3 - Q_1)}{Q_2}$$

The expression 'extreme value' has been referred to several times already and, as was explained in section 4.2, such extreme values are often termed **outliers**. Although a complete treatment of outliers is beyond the scope of this book it is worth exploring another simple way of deciding whether or not a value is an outlier. Again this should be treated as a rule-of-thumb, although in chapter 9 you will realise why it is useful.

The rule requires the evaluation of $\dfrac{x - \mu}{\sigma}$ or $\dfrac{x - \bar{x}}{s}$ and then if the value obtained is greater than 2 or less than -2 the value x can be considered to be an outlier or extreme value.

Exercise 4A

1 (a) Find the range of the following set of board game scores:

8 18 7 16 19 8 11 18 22 9 10 14 11 15 16 24

(b) For the same data find:

(i) the upper and lower quartiles

(ii) the interquartile range

(iii) the semi-interquartile range.

2 For each of the following samples, estimate the mean and the standard deviation of the population:

(a) 17   16   15   22   13   20   13   18   24   18

(b)

Number	12	13	14	15	16	17	18
Frequency	90	150	240	290	160	70	0

(c)

Class	7–10	11–14	15–18	19–22	23–26	27–30
Frequency	1	3	9	15	14	8

3 A class of 6 children sat a test; the resulting marks, scored out of 10, were as follows:

$$4 \quad 5 \quad 6 \quad 8 \quad 4 \quad 9$$

Calculate the mean and the variance of this population

4 A health clinic wished to check the daily milk consumption of its 160 clients. Each client recorded their intake of milk (in ml) during a given day. The results were summarised as follows:

Milk intake (ml)	Number of clients
0–24	2
25–49	6
50–99	42
100–149	56
150–199	22
200–299	22
300–499	10

Estimate the mean and the standard deviation of the milk intake of this population.

5 A student visits a shop frequently. On twenty random occasions she recorded the queue length (the number of people queueing) at the check-out. The results were as follows:

Queue length	4	5	6	7	8	9
Number of visits	2	3	7	6	0	2

Estimate the mean and the standard deviation of the queue length at this shop.

6 The numbers of errors, x, on each of 200 pages of typescript was monitored. The results when summarised showed that:

$$\sum x = 920 \qquad \sum x^2 = 5032$$

Calculate the mean and the standard deviation of the number of errors per page. [E]

7 The stem and leaf diagram below represents data collected for the number of insects caught in an insect trap each day for 4 weeks.

Number of insects			0	1 means 1
0	1 1 2	(3)		
1	2 3 5 5 5 6	(6)		
2	2 2 3 5 8 8	(6)		
3	4 4 4 4 5 7 7 9	(8)		
4	2 6 7 7 8	(5)		

(a) Draw a box and whisker plot for these data.

(b) Using your plot to help you, comment on the skewness of the distribution.

8 The number of birds visiting a bird table was counted each minute for 15 minutes. The distribution was as follows:

9   4   7   5   3   8   6   5   8   10   5   6   5   8   10

Find the mode, median and mean of these data and use them to comment on the skewness of this distribution.

9 Skewness can be quantitatively assessed by using

$$\frac{3\,(\text{mean} - \text{median})}{\text{standard deviation}}$$

Calculate this numerical measure of skewness for the following distribution which shows ages of patients in a hospital ward.

58   39   30   48   27   16   56   56   65   63

Comment on the skewness of this distribution.

10 For the data sets below identify any outliers and draw a box plot. To find the outliers use $1.5\,(Q_3 - Q_1)$.

(a) 11   13   14   18   29   17   10   12   11   17   16

(b) 27   31   15   43   39   57   33   27

(c) 51   55   59   35   81   50   52   61   77   57   51   60

11 The students in a class were each asked to write down how many CDs they owned. The student with the least number of CDs had 14 and all but one of the others owned 60 or fewer. The remaining student owned 65. The quartiles for the class were 30, 34 and 42 respectively.

Outliers are defined to be any values outside the limits of $1.5(Q_3 - Q_1)$ below the lower quartile or above the upper quartile.

On graph paper draw a box plot to represent these data, indicating clearly any outliers. [E]

12 The number of bags of potato crisps sold per day in a bar was recorded over a two-week period. The results are shown below.

      20, 15, 10, 30, 33, 40, 5, 11, 13, 20, 25, 42, 31, 17

(a) Calculate the mean of these data.

(b) Draw a stem and leaf diagram to represent these data.

(c) Find the median and the quartiles of these data.

An outlier is an observation that falls either 1.5 × (interquartile range) above the upper quartile or 1.5 × (interquartile range) below the lower quartile.

(d) Determine whether or not any items of data are outliers.

(e) On graph paper draw a box plot to represent these data. Show your scale clearly.

(f) Comment on the skewness of the distribution of bags of crisps sold per day. Justify your answer.

13 A travel agent sells holidays from his shop. The price, in £, of 15 holidays sold on a particular day are shown below.

299	1050	2315	999	485
350	169	1015	650	830
99	2100	689	550	475

For these data, find

(a) the mean and the standard deviation,

(b) the median and the inter-quartile range.

An outlier is an observation that falls either more than 1.5 × (inter-quartile range) above the upper quartile or more than 1.5 × (inter-quartile range) below the lower quartile.

(c) Determine if any of the prices are outliers.

On the same day, the travel agent recorded the price, £x, of each of 20 holidays sold on his website. The cheapest holiday sold was £98, the most expensive was £2400 and the quartiles of these data were £305, £1379 and £1805. There were no outliers.

(d) On graph paper, and using the same scale, draw box plots for the holidays sold in the shop and the holidays sold on the website.

(e) Compare and contrast sales from the shop and sales from the website. [E]

SUMMARY OF KEY POINTS

1 The range of a data set is given by:

   Range = largest value − smallest value

2 The interquartile range is given by:

   $$\text{IQR} = Q_3 - Q_1$$

3 The semi-interquartile range is defined as:

   $$\text{SIQR} = \tfrac{1}{2}(Q_3 - Q_1)$$

4 Variance of a population is defined as:

   $$\sigma^2 = \frac{\sum(x - \mu)^2}{n} \qquad \text{or} \qquad \sigma^2 = \frac{\sum f(x - \mu)^2}{\sum f}$$

5 Unbiased estimator of the population variance is defined as:

   $$s^2 = \frac{\sum(x - \bar{x})^2}{n - 1} \qquad \text{or} \qquad s^2 = \frac{\sum f(x - \bar{x})^2}{\sum f - 1}$$

6 The standard deviation is the positive square root of the variance.

7 For positive skew: $Q_2 - Q_1 \ < \ Q_3 - Q_2$
      negative skew: $Q_2 - Q_1 \ > \ Q_3 - Q_2$
      symmetry: $Q_2 - Q_1 \ = \ Q_3 - Q_2$

Probability

5.1 Elementary probability

We live in a world full of uncertainty and describe this in many different ways.

> "I *should* be back by 10 pm."
> "John is *sure* to be in the team."
> "I *might* just scrape a pass in economics."

Each of these phrases expresses a degree of uncertainty. To deal with uncertainty mathematically you need to be able to express it as a number. You can do this by using a scale from 0 to 1 to describe the *chance* that something will happen. On this scale 0 represents a situation which is impossible and 1 represents something that is certain to happen. This number is called the **probability** that something will happen.

- **Probability – If p is a probability then $0 \leqslant p \leqslant 1$**

In the situations described in the phrases above there is no obvious way for arriving at a value for the probability that each one will happen. You could ask someone involved in these incidents to estimate what they think the value of the probability will be. This would give you a **subjective probability** – one which depends on the judgement of the person making the estimate. This can be useful in such situations, but sometimes there are other ways of estimating a probability.

At the start of a cricket match two captains toss a coin to decide who should bat first. What is the probability that the coin will land heads up? The coin could land on its edge, but that is very unlikely, so you could argue that there are only two realistic possibilities – heads up and tails up. Both of these are **equally likely** so you could say that the probability of the coin landing heads up is 0.5 (halfway between 0 and 1 on the probability scale).

An alternative method for finding a value for this probability for any coin is to toss that coin a large number of times and calculate the ratio:

$$\frac{\text{number of times it lands heads}}{\text{number of tosses}}$$

This is called the **relative frequency** of the coin landing heads up because it is a measure *relative* to the total number of tosses. Plotting a graph of the relative frequency against the number of tosses gives something like this:

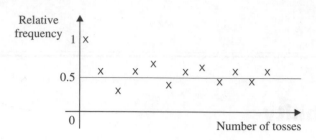

As the number of tosses increases the relative frequency gets closer and closer to a particular value – it tends to a limit. You could use this value as an estimate of the probability that the coin will land heads up.

So there are various ways of arriving at a value for a probability. Most of the work on probability in this chapter assumes that the probabilities of different situations are already known and is about combining probabilities.

5.2 The terminology of probability

Venn diagrams

To introduce the terminology commonly used when studying probability imagine a school which has 100 students in its sixth form – 50 students study mathematics, 29 study biology and 13 study both subjects. A convenient method of summarising this information is to use a **Venn diagram**:

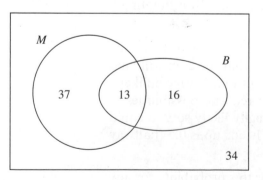

Notice how the $50 - 13 = 37$ students who study mathematics but not biology and the $100 - 37 - 13 - 16 = 34$ students who do not study either subject are represented.

Suppose you went into the sixth form common room one break and picked a student at random. What is the probability that this student studies mathematics? We call this process of walking into the room and selecting a student at random an **experiment**. An experiment must be capable of being repeated as many times as you like under essentially the same conditions.

Sample space

Though you cannot say for certain what the outcome of any one experiment will be, you can list all the possible outcomes and this list is called the **sample space**.

An **event** is a group or set of possible outcomes from such an experiment. Capital letters are usually used to label events, for example M for the event that the student selected studies mathematics. From the Venn diagram the probability that the student studies mathematics is:

$$\frac{37 + 13}{100} = \frac{1}{2}$$

This can be written $\qquad$ $P(M) = \frac{1}{2}$

In a similar way we can define the event B that the student studies biology and find that:

$$P(B) = \frac{29}{100}$$

The probability that the student studies *both* mathematics *and* biology can be written as

$$P(M \cap B) = \frac{13}{100}$$

The probability that the student studies mathematics *or* biology can be written as

$$P(M \cup B) = \frac{37 + 13 + 16}{100} = \frac{66}{100} = \frac{33}{50}$$

Notice that 'or' in mathematics includes the possibility of 'both'.

Other probabilities can easily be read off from the Venn diagram. For example the probability that the student *does not* study biology is:

$$P(B') = \frac{37 + 34}{100} = \frac{71}{100}$$

Notice that B' is the event *not B*.

Similarly the probability that the student studies biology but not mathematics is

$$P(B \cap M') = \frac{16}{100} = \frac{4}{25}$$

$P(B')$ can also be found using the relationship:

$$P(B') = 1 - P(B)$$

$$= 1 - \tfrac{29}{100} = \tfrac{71}{100}$$

■ **Complementary probability** – If A' represents the event not A then $P(A') = 1 - P(A)$

5.3 Addition rule

The above example shows that:

$$P(M \text{ or } B) = P(M) + P(B) - P(\text{both } M \text{ and } B)$$

$$\tfrac{66}{100} = \tfrac{50}{100} + \tfrac{29}{100} - \tfrac{13}{100}$$

Notice that the probability of the student studying mathematics and the probability of the student studying biology each include the probability of the student studying *both* mathematics and biology. To obtain the probability of studying mathematics *or* biology you only need to include this probability of *both* once, hence the extra case is subtracted.

So a general rule for events A and B is:

■ **Addition rule** $P(A \cup B) = P(A) + P(B) - P(A \cap B)$

Example 1

In a mathematics test there are two questions on algebra. The probability of a student getting the first question correct is 0.6 and the probability of getting the second question correct is also 0.6 but the probability of getting both correct is 0.3. A student is recorded as having passed in algebra if either (or both) of the questions are correct. Find the probability that the student records a pass in algebra.

Let Q_1 represent the event "the student gets the first question correct" and
Q_2 represent the event "the student gets the second question correct"

The probability that a pass in algebra is recorded is

$$P(Q_1 \cup Q_2)$$

Now $$P(Q_1 \cup Q_2) = P(Q_1) + P(Q_2) - P(Q_1 \cap Q_2)$$

$$= 0.6 + 0.6 - 0.3$$

$$= 0.9$$

Exercise 5A

1   In a certain class of 30 primary school children there are 16 girls. There are 7 girls and 6 boys with fair hair. A pupil is selected at random to be the class captain. Find the probability that the class captain
   (a) is a girl
   (b) is a boy with fair hair
   (c) has not got fair hair
   (d) is a girl and has not got fair hair.

2   A card is selected at random from a normal set of 52 playing cards. Let Q be the event that the card is a queen and D the event that the card is a diamond. Find:
   (a) $P(Q \cap D)$ (b) $P(Q \cup D)$
   (c) $P(Q' \cup D)$ (d) $P(Q \cap D')$.
   Describe in words the probabilities:
   (e) $P(Q' \cap D) = \frac{12}{52} = \frac{3}{13}$ (f) $P(Q' \cap D') = \frac{36}{52} = \frac{9}{13}$.

3   An archer has two attempts to hit a target. The probability that his first arrow hits is 0.4 and the probability that the second arrow hits is 0.5. Given that the probability that he hits the target with both arrows is 0.2, find the probability that he misses the target with both arrows.

4   If A and B are two events and $P(A) = 0.6$, $P(B) = 0.3$ and $P(A \cup B) = 0.8$, find:
   (a) $P(A \cap B)$ (b) $P(A' \cap B)$ (c) $P(A \cap B')$
   (d) $P(A' \cap B')$ (e) $P(A \cup B')$ (f) $P(A' \cup B)$.

5   If S and T are two events and $P(T) = 0.4$, $P(S \cap T) = 0.15$ and $P(S' \cap T') = 0.5$, find:
   (a) $P(S \cap T')$ (b) $P(S)$ (c) $P(S \cup T)$
   (d) $P(S' \cap T)$ (e) $P(S' \cup T')$.

6   The events M and N are such that $P(M) = P(N) = 2P(M \cap N)$. Given that $P(M \cup N) = 0.6$, find:
   (a) $P(M \cap N)$ (b) $P(M)$ (c) $P(M' \cap N')$
   (d) $P(M \cap N')$.

7 A student going into the common room reads *Private Eye* with probability 0.75, *Private Eye* but not the *Daily Express* with probability 0.65. The student reads neither with probability 0.20.
(a) Find the probability that the student reads both *Private Eye* and the *Daily Express*.
(b) Find the probability that the student reads the *Daily Express* but not *Private Eye*. [E]

8 Of the households in Edinburgh, 35% have a freezer and 60% have a colour TV set. Given that 25% of the households have both a freezer and a colour TV set, calculate the probability that a household has either a freezer or a colour TV set but not both. [E]

9 In a large group of people it is known that 10% have a hot breakfast, 20% have a hot lunch and 25% have a hot breakfast or a hot lunch. Find the probability that a person chosen at random from this group has a hot breakfast and a hot lunch. [E]

10 The carburettor for a particular motor car is manufactured at one of three factories X, Y, Z and then delivered to the main assembly line. Factory X supplies 45% of the total number of carburettors to the line, factory Y 30% and factory Z 25%. Of the carburettors manufactured at factory X, 2% are faulty and the corresponding percentages for factories Y and Z are 4% and 3% respectively.
Let X, Y and Z represent the events that a carburettor chosen at random from the assembly line was manufactured at factory X, Y or Z respectively and let F denote the event that this carburettor is faulty.
(a) Express in words the meaning of $Y \cap F'$ and of $Y \cup Z$.
(b) Calculate $P(X \cap F)$, $P(Y \cap F)$ and $P(Z \cap F)$.
(c) Sketch a Venn diagram to illustrate the events X, Y, Z and F. Include in your diagram the probabilities corresponding to the different regions within the diagram.
(d) Find the probability that a carburettor, selected at random from the main assembly line, is faulty. [E]

5.4 Multiplication rule

Consider again the subjects studied by a school's sixth form students, which was summarised as follows:

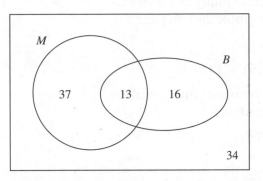

Suppose now that instead of going into the sixth form common room and selecting a student at random from the group of 100, you went into the biology department and selected a student at random from the 29 biologists. What is the probability that this student also studies mathematics?

The probability is written as:

$$P(M|B)$$

and read as:

"the probability of the student studying mathematics *given that* the student studies biology".

This is an example of a **conditional probability**:

the probability of *M* (the student studying mathematics) *conditional* upon the event *B* (the student studying biology) having already happened.

In this example

$$P(M|B) = \frac{13}{29}$$

as there are 13 of the 29 biology students who also study mathematics.

Notice that the 13 in the numerator represents the students in $\{M \cap B\}$ and the 29 in the denominator those in *B*. So this could be written as:

$$P(M|B) = \frac{P(M \cap B)}{P(B)} = \frac{\frac{13}{100}}{\frac{29}{100}} = \frac{13}{29}$$

which can also be written as:

$$P(M \cap B) = P(M|B) \times P(B)$$

Notice that we could write

$$P(M \cap B) = P(B|M) \times P(M)$$

(in this example that is $\frac{13}{100} = \frac{13}{50} \times \frac{50}{100}$).

The reordering of events in a conditional probability is sometimes useful in more complicated situations (see example 2(c) on page 77).

So for two events A and B:

- **Multiplication rule** $P(A \cap B) = P(A|B) \times P(B)$

Sometimes a dot $\cdot$ is used instead of $\times$ to represent multiplication and in this case the multiplication rule is written

$$P(A \cap B) = P(A|B) \cdot P(B)$$

Tree diagrams

Consider a bag that contains 5 black and 3 yellow beads. A bead is selected at random from the bag and retained. A second bead is then selected from the remaining 7 beads. (This is an example of sampling without replacement and is discussed in more detail on page 83).

Let B_1 stand for the event "the first bead was black" and B_2 the event "the second bead was black", similarly the events Y_1 and Y_2 can be defined to stand for the first and second beads being yellow. The above events can be represented using a **tree diagram**:

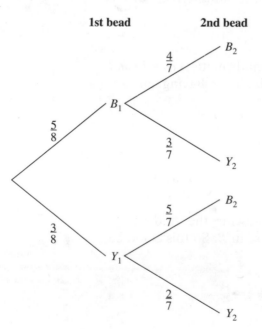

Probabilities are written along the branches. Notice that the probabilities on the second tier of branches are conditional probabilities, for example, $P(B_2 \mid B_1)$ is $\frac{4}{7}$. The probability that both beads are black:

$$P(B_1 \cap B_2)$$

is found using the multiplication rule as:

$$P(B_1 \cap B_2) = P(B_2|B_1) \times P(B_1) = \frac{4}{7} \times \frac{5}{8} = \frac{5}{14}$$

The probability that both beads are the *same* colour is:

$$P(B_1 \cap B_2) + P(Y_1 \cap Y_2) = \frac{5}{14} + \frac{3}{8} \times \frac{2}{7} = \frac{13}{28}$$

To understand why these probabilities are *added*, let $C = B_1 \cap B_2$ (i.e. the event both beads are black) and $D = Y_1 \cap Y_2$ (i.e. the event both beads are yellow). The probability that both beads are black *or* both are yellow is written as:

$$P(C \cup D).$$

Now by the addition rule this gives:

$$P(C \cup D) = P(C) + P(D) - P(C \cap D)$$

but the event $C \cap D$ is impossible (since both beads cannot be black and yellow at the same time) so:

$$P(C \cap D) = 0$$

and the required probability is:

$$P(C) + P(D) = \frac{5}{14} + \frac{3}{28} = \frac{13}{28}$$

(This is an example of mutually exclusive events which are discussed on page 82.)

A useful rule for using tree diagrams is:

multiply *along* the branches and *add* between branches.

Example 2

A certain medical disease occurs in 1% of the population. A simple screening procedure is available and in 8 out of 10 cases where the patient has the disease, it produces a positive result. If the patient does not have the disease there is still a 0.05 chance that the test will give a positive result. Find the probability that a randomly selected individual:

(a) does not have the disease but gives a positive result in the screening test
(b) gives a positive result on the test.

Ann has taken the test and her result is positive.

(c) Find the probability that she has the disease.

Let C represent the event "the patient has the disease" and
S represent the event "the screening test gives a positive result".

A tree diagram of the information in the question gives:

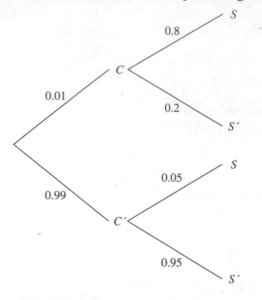

(a) The probability that the patient does not have the disease but gives a positive screening result is:

$$P(C' \cap S) = 0.99 \times 0.05$$
$$= 0.0495$$

(b) The probability that the patient gives a positive test result is:
$$P(S) = P(C \cap S) + P(C' \cap S)$$
$$= 0.01 \times 0.8 + 0.0495$$
$$= 0.0575$$

(c) The probability that Ann has the disease is:
$$P(C|S) = \frac{P(C \cap S)}{P(S)}$$
$$= \frac{0.01 \times 0.8}{0.0575}$$
$$= 0.139 \text{ (to 3 decimal places)}$$

Exercise 5B

1 A bag contains 6 red and 4 blue beads. A bead is picked out and retained and then a second bead is picked out. Find the probability that:
   (a) both beads are red
   (b) the beads are of different colours
   (c) the second bead is red given that the first one is blue.

2 A teacher calculates that if a student regularly completes their homework the probability that they will pass the examination is 0.8 and that if the student does not do the homework the probability of passing is only 0.4. Given that only 75% of the students do their homework regularly, calculate the probability that a randomly selected student:

(a) does not do the homework regularly and passes the examination

(b) passes the examination.

3 A certain statistician's breakfast consists of either some cereal or toast (but not both) to eat and one drink from a choice of fruit juice, tea or coffee. If he has cereal to eat, the probability that he chooses coffee is $\frac{3}{5}$ and the probability he chooses tea is $\frac{3}{10}$. If he has toast to eat, the probability he chooses coffee is $\frac{2}{5}$ and the probability he chooses tea is $\frac{1}{5}$. Given that he has cereal with probability $\frac{3}{4}$:

(a) find the probability that on any particular day he has

(i) fruit juice   (ii) cereal and coffee.

(b) Find his most popular breakfast combination.

4 Given that $P(A) = 0.7$, $P(B) = 0.4$ and $P(A \cup B) = 0.8$, find the following:

(a) $P(A \cap B)$ (b) $P(A|B)$ (c) $P(B|A)$ (d) $P(A|B')$.

5 Given $P(R|S) = 0.5$, $P(R|S') = 0.4$ and $P(S) = 0.6$, find:

(a) $P(R)$ (b) $P(S|R)$ (c) $P(S'|R)$ (d) $P(S'|R')$.

6 In year 11 of a certain school 55% of the pupils are boys. Of the boys 80% stay on into the sixth form but only 75% of the girls do.

(a) Find the probability that a randomly selected pupil from year 11 is a girl who stays on into the sixth form.

(b) Find the probability that a randomly chosen year 11 pupil will not stay on into the sixth form.

(c) Find the probability that a randomly selected sixth form pupil is a girl.

7 A bunch of 30 keys are either gold or silver in colour (but not both). There are 10 mortice lock keys and 20 yale lock keys. Of these 5 yale lock and 2 mortice lock keys are gold in colour. A key is selected at random.

(a) Find the probability that the key is silver in colour.

(b) Find the probability that the key is silver coloured and for a mortice lock.

I borrow this bunch of keys to open a yale lock.

(c) What is the probability that the correct key is silver?

8 Let A and B be events such that $P(A) = \frac{1}{4}$, $P(B) = \frac{1}{3}$ and $P(A \cup B) = \frac{5}{12}$.

(a) Find $P(A|B)$ and $P(A|B')$.

(b) Find $P(A|B)\, P(B) + P(A|B')\, P(B')$.

Comment on your result. [E]

9 A teacher walks, cycles or drives to school with probabilities 0.1, 0.3 and 0.6 respectively. If she walks to school she has a probability of 0.35 of being late. The corresponding probabilities of being late if she cycles or drives to school are 0.1 and 0.55 respectively.

(a) Find the probability that she is late on any particular day.

(b) Given that she is late one day, find the probability that she walked.

(c) Given that she is not late one day, find the probability that she walked.

Give your answers to 3 decimal places. [E]

10 State in words the meaning of the symbol $P(B|A)$, where A and B are two events.

A shop stocks tinned cat food of two makes A and B, and two sizes, large and small. Of the stock, 70% is of brand A, 30% is of brand B. Of the tins of brand A, 30% are small size whilst of the tins of brand B, 40% are small size. Using a tree diagram, or otherwise, find the probability that:

(a) a tin chosen at random from the stock will be of small size

(b) a small tin chosen at random from the stock will be of brand A. [E]

11 A boy always either walks to school or goes by bus. If one day he goes to school by bus, then the probability that he goes by bus the next day is $\frac{7}{10}$. If one day he walks to school, then the probability that he goes by bus the next day is $\frac{2}{5}$.

(a) Given that he walks to school on a particular Tuesday, draw a tree diagram and hence find the probability that he will go to school by bus on Thursday of that week.

(b) Given that the boy walks to school on both Tuesday and Thursday of that week, find the probability that he will also walk to school on Wednesday.

(You may assume that the boy will not be absent from school on Wednesday or Thursday of that week.) [E]

12 For married couples the probability that the husband has passed his driving test is $\frac{7}{10}$ and the probability that the wife has passed her driving test is $\frac{1}{2}$. The probability that the husband has passed, given that the wife has passed, is $\frac{14}{15}$. Find the probability that, for a randomly chosen married couple, the driving test will have been passed by:

(a) both of them

(b) only one of them

(c) neither of them.

If two married couples are chosen at random, find the probability that only one of the husbands and only one of the wives will have passed the driving test. [E]

5.5 Independent and mutually exclusive events

If you roll two fair dice, a yellow one and a red one, the possible outcomes could be represented by crosses in the following diagram:

The set of crosses inside the loop ⊂⊃ represents the event Y, that the yellow die shows a six, and the set of crosses inside the rectangle ⊓ represents the event R, that the red die shows a six.

Since there are 36 possible outcomes (and they are all equally likely) then

$$P(Y) = \tfrac{1}{6}, \; P(R) = \tfrac{1}{6} \text{ and } P(Y \cap R) = \tfrac{1}{36}.$$

Notice that in this situation the event Y is not going to influence the event R. So Y and R are **independent** events and the probability of Y *given that* R has happened will be the same as the probability of Y. This is written as:

$$P(Y|R) = P(Y)$$

Using the multiplication rule this gives:

$$P(Y \cap R) = P(Y) \times P(R)$$

and this is the usual definition for independent events. Notice that in this example $\tfrac{1}{36} = \tfrac{1}{6} \times \tfrac{1}{6}$.

■ **If two events A and B are independent**
   $P(A \cap B) = P(A) \times P(B)$.

Now let E be the event that the number showing on the yellow die and the number showing on the red die are equal. This is indicated in the diagram below by ╲.

Let S represent the event that the sum of the number showing on the yellow die and the number showing on the red die is 7. This is indicated by ╱ below.

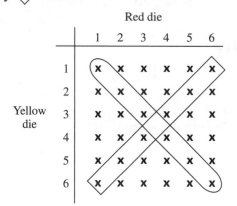

From the diagram it is clear that:

$$P(E) = \tfrac{1}{6} \text{ and } P(S) = \tfrac{1}{6} \quad \text{but} \quad P(E \cap S) = 0$$

since if the numbers on the dice are equal then their sum can *never* be 7. So E and S are **mutually exclusive** events because they cannot both happen together.

■ **If A and B are mutually exclusive events**
   $P(A \cap B) = 0$.

Notice that E and S are not independent events since $P(E) \times P(S) \neq P(E \cap S)$.

Example 3

In a certain group of 15 students, 5 have graphics calculators and 3 have a computer at home (one student has both). Two of the students drive themselves to college each day and neither of them has a graphics calculator nor a computer at home. A student is selected at random from the group.

(a) Find the probability that the student either drives to college or has a graphics calculator.

(b) Show that the events "the student has a graphics calculator" and "the student has a computer at home" are independent.

Let G represent the event "the student has a graphics calculator",
   H represent the event "the student has a computer at home"
   and
   D represent the event "the student drives to college each day".

The information in the question can be represented in a Venn diagram, as follows:

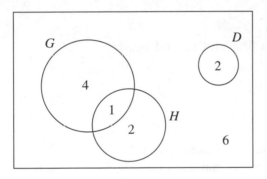

(a) The probability that the student either drives or has a graphics calculator is $P(G \cup D)$.

Notice that G and D are mutually exclusive events so
$P(G \cap D) = 0$.

$$\therefore \qquad P(G \cup D) = P(G) + P(D)$$
$$= \tfrac{5}{15} + \tfrac{2}{15}$$
$$= \tfrac{7}{15}$$

(b) From the diagram:

$$P(G \cap H) = \tfrac{1}{15}, P(G) = \tfrac{5}{15} = \tfrac{1}{3} \text{ and } P(H) = \tfrac{3}{15} = \tfrac{1}{5}$$

Since $P(G) \times P(H) = P(G \cap H)$, the events G and H are independent.

The independence of two events is often connected with the *method* of sampling. The example on page 76 considered the selection of two beads from a bag containing 5 black and 3 yellow beads. In that example the first bead was *retained* before the second bead was selected. This is an example of **sampling without replacement**.

Consider again the tree diagram which represents the events in the example:

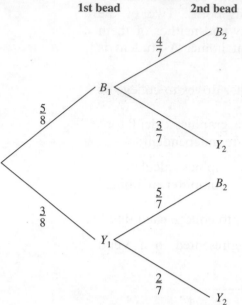

Notice that the events B_1 and B_2 (that the first and second beads were black) are *not* independent for

$$P(B_2|B_1) = \tfrac{4}{7}$$

but

$$P(B_2) = \tfrac{5}{8} \times \tfrac{4}{7} + \tfrac{3}{8} \times \tfrac{5}{7} = \tfrac{5}{8}$$

If the first bead is *replaced* before the next one is selected so that the total number of beads from which the selection is made remains the same, this is called **sampling with replacement** and results in the following tree diagram:

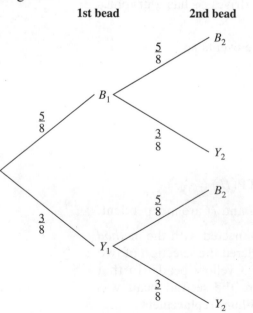

The events B_1 and B_2 are now independent for

$$P(B_2) = \tfrac{5}{8} \times \tfrac{5}{8} + \tfrac{3}{8} \times \tfrac{5}{8} = \tfrac{5}{8}$$

and

$$P(B_1 \cap B_2) = \tfrac{5}{8} \times \tfrac{5}{8} = P(B_1) \times P(B_2)$$

Exercise 5C

1 Two archers each independently fire an arrow at a target.
   The probability that the first archer hits the target is 0.6 and
   the probability that the second archer hits the target is 0.7.
   (a) Find the probability that they both hit the target.
   (b) Find the probability that the target is hit by at least one
   of them.

2 In a game at a fair, contestants are given two darts and have
   to burst a balloon by throwing a dart to hit it. If they burst
   the balloon with the first dart the second dart is not used.
   Given that the probability of bursting the balloon with the
   first dart is 0.3 and, if the first time they miss, the probability
   of bursting it the second time is 0.4, find the probability that
   they burst the balloon.

3 Helen loves cuddly toys. The probability that her
   grandmother buys her a cuddly toy for her birthday is 0.8
   and the probability that her grandfather buys her a cuddly
   toy is 0.7. Assuming that her grandparents do not liaise over
   the matter of birthday presents, find the probability that
   Helen receives a cuddly toy for her birthday.

4 A red and a yellow die are thrown and the events A, B and C
   are defined as follows:
   $A =$ the yellow die shows a 5
   $B =$ the sum of the scores of the two dice is 5
   $C =$ the red die shows a 5.
   (a) Find:
   (i) $P(A)$ (ii) $P(B)$ (iii) $P(C)$
   (iv) $P(A \cap B)$ (v) $P(B \cap C)$ (vi) $P(A \cap C)$.
   (b) Which event is mutually exclusive to A?
   (c) Which event is independent of A?

5 There are 15 books on a bookshelf. There are 10 books of fiction, 4 of which are hard-back. There are 6 hard-back books on the shelf, the other 9 are all paper-backs. One book is selected at random from the shelf.

(a) Find the probability that the book is a hard-back book of fiction.

(b) Find the probability that a hard-back book is selected.

(c) Find the probability that the book selected is a book of fiction.

(d) Find the probability that a paper-back is selected.

(e) Describe a pair of independent events.

6 The events A and B are independent and $P(A) = 0.3$ and $P(B) = 0.5$. Find:

(a) $P(A \cup B)$ (b) $P(A')$ (c) $P(A' \cap B)$

7 The events A and B have $P(A) = 0.2$, $P(B) = 0.5$ and $P(A \cup B) = 0.6$. Find:

(a) $P(A \cap B)$ (b) $P(A|B)$ (c) $P(B|A)$.

8 A cubical die is relabelled so that it has 3 ones, 2 twos and 1 six. The die is rolled and R is the event that the number showing is 2 and Q is the event that the number showing is even. Find:

(a) $P(Q)$ (b) $P(R)$ (c) $P(Q')$ (d) $P(R')$

(e) $P(R \cap Q)$ (f) $P(R \cap Q')$ (g) $P(R' \cap Q)$.

(h) Write down a pair of mutually exclusive events.

9 A and B are two independent events such that $P(A) = \alpha$ and $P(A \cup B) = \beta$, $\beta > \alpha$. Show that:

$$P(B) = \frac{\beta - \alpha}{1 - \alpha}$$ [E]

10 A and B are two independent events such that $P(A) = 0.2$ and $P(B) = 0.15$.

Evaluate the following probabilities.

(a) $P(A|B)$ (b) $P(A \cap B)$ (c) $P(A \cup B)$.   [E]

11 Seven identical balls are marked respectively with the numbers 1 to 7 inclusive. The number on each ball represents the score for that ball. The seven balls are then put into a bag. If 2 balls are chosen at random one after the other, find the probability of obtaining a total score of 11 or more:

(a) if the first ball is replaced

(b) if the first ball is not replaced.

If 2 balls are chosen at random one after the other from the 7 balls find, in case (a) and in case (b), the most probable total score for the 2 balls with its associated probability. [E]

12 State in words the relationship between two events E and F when:

(a) $P(E \cap F) = P(E).P(F)$

(b) $P(E \cap F) = 0$.

Given that $P(E) = \frac{1}{3}$, $P(F) = \frac{1}{2}$, $P(E' \cap F) = \frac{1}{2}$, find:

(c) the relationship between E and F

(d) the value of $P(E|F)$

(e) the value of $P(E' \cap F')$. [E]

13 An urn contains 3 red, 4 white and 5 blue discs. Three discs are selected at random from the urn. Find the probability that:

(a) all three discs are the same colour, if the selection is with replacement

(b) all three discs are of different colours, if the selection is without replacement. [E]

14 Show that, for any two events E and F:

$$P(E \cup F) = P(E) + P(F) - P(E \cap F).$$

Express in words the meaning of $P(E|F)$.

Given that E and F are independent events, express $P(E \cap F)$ in terms of $P(E)$ and $P(F)$, and show that E' and F are also independent.

In a college, 60 students are studying one or more of the three subjects Geography, French and English. Of these, 25 are studying Geography, 26 are studying French, 44 are studying English, 10 are studying Geography and French, 15 are studying French and English, and 16 are studying Geography and English.

Write down the probability that a student chosen at random from those studying English is also studying French.

Determine whether or not the events "studying Geography" and "studying French" are independent.

A student is chosen at random from all 60 students. Find the probability that the chosen student is studying all three subjects. [E]

5.6 Number of arrangements

Although you will not require a detailed understanding of permutations and combinations in S1 you will sometimes need to be able to calculate the number of arrangements of a set of objects. This will be used in the work on the binomial distribution in Book S2, but could also occur in probability questions such as the following.

A bag contains 7 red and 3 blue beads. Three beads are selected at random from the bag without replacement. The possible outcomes to the experiment can be illustrated with a tree diagram.

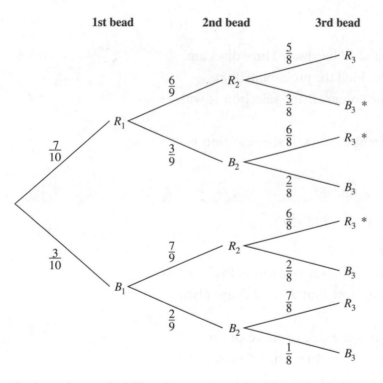

To calculate the probability that two red beads and one blue bead are selected, we simply consider the three cases marked*:

$$R_1 R_2 B_3 \qquad R_1 B_2 R_3 \qquad B_1 R_2 R_3$$

with corresponding probabilities

$$\tfrac{7}{10} \times \tfrac{6}{9} \times \tfrac{3}{8} \qquad \tfrac{7}{10} \times \tfrac{3}{9} \times \tfrac{6}{8} \qquad \tfrac{3}{10} \times \tfrac{7}{9} \times \tfrac{6}{8}$$

Now you should notice that the probabilities for each of these three cases are the same and so the answer to the question: 'What is the probability that there are 2 red beads and 1 blue bead?' is:

$$3 \times \tfrac{7}{10} \times \tfrac{6}{9} \times \tfrac{3}{8} = \tfrac{21}{40} \quad \text{or} \quad 0.525$$

Now a quicker way of arriving at this result is to reason as follows. We require two reds and a blue, i.e. *RRB*. The probability of selecting them in that order, i.e. $R_1 R_2 B_3$ is

$$\tfrac{7}{10} \times \tfrac{6}{9} \times \tfrac{3}{8}$$

but there are other possible orders too, and we need to find how many possible arrangements there are of two reds and one blue. In this case it is fairly simple. Think of how many positions the *B* can take and the three arrangements can be seen:

$$R_1 R_2 B_3$$
$$R_1 B_2 R_3$$
$$B_1 R_2 R_3$$

We have seen from the tree diagram that the probabilities for each of these cases are the same so the required probability is

$$3 \times \tfrac{7}{10} \times \tfrac{6}{9} \times \tfrac{3}{8}$$

Suppose four beads are chosen, then the probability of two red and two blue can be found as follows. Firstly, find the probability of selecting them in the order *RRBB*.

Then $\qquad P(R_1 R_2 B_3 B_4) = \tfrac{7}{10} \times \tfrac{6}{9} \times \tfrac{3}{8} \times \tfrac{2}{7}$

Then we need to calculate the number of arrangements of two *R*s and two *B*s.

There are six of these:

RRBB	*BBRR*
RBRB	*BRBR*
RBBR	*BRRB*
Keep first *R* fixed and move second to different positions	then swap *B*s and *R*s

So the probability of two red beads and two blue beads when four are selected is

$$6 \times \tfrac{7}{10} \times \tfrac{6}{9} \times \tfrac{3}{8} \times \tfrac{2}{7} = \tfrac{3}{10} \quad \text{or} \quad 0.3$$

Example 4

A bag contains 6 blue balls, 5 green balls and 4 red balls. Three are selected at random without replacement. Find the probability that

(a) they are all blue,
(b) two are blue and one is green,
(c) there is one of each colour.

(a) The required sequence is *BBB* and there is only one arrangement with probability

$$\tfrac{6}{15} \times \tfrac{5}{14} \times \tfrac{4}{13} = \tfrac{4}{91}$$

(b) Consider selection in the order BBG:

$$P(B_1 B_2 G_3) = \frac{6}{15} \times \frac{5}{14} \times \frac{5}{13} = \frac{5}{91}$$

But there are three arrangements of two Bs and one G: BBG, BGB and GBB.

So the probability is $3 \times \frac{5}{91} = \frac{15}{91}$.

(c) Consider selection in the order BGR.

$$P(B_1 G_2 R_3) = \frac{6}{15} \times \frac{5}{14} \times \frac{4}{13} = \frac{4}{91}$$

But there are six arrangements of one B, one G and one R (BGR, BRG, GBR, GRB, RBG and RGB; two cases with each letter first).

So the probability is $6 \times \frac{4}{91} = \frac{24}{91}$.

In Book S2 the factorial notation will be introduced and a formula for calculating the number of arrangements in a more complicated situation will be given.

Exercise 5D

1 A bag contains 3 blue balls, 6 green balls and 5 red balls. Three are selected at random without replacement. Find the probability that:
(a) they are all green,
(b) two are red and one is blue,
(c) there is one of each colour.

2 A game is played with four fair dice. Each die is rolled once and the number of sixes is noted. Find the probability that:
(a) there is just one six,
(b) there are only two sixes,
(c) there are exactly two sixes given that there were no sixes in the first two rolls.

3 John has a CD collection consisting of 5 recordings of brass bands, 8 of opera and 7 of country and western music. In a rush to go on holiday he randomly selects three CDs to take with him. Find the probability that
(a) all three CDs are of brass bands,
(b) there are two of brass bands and one of country and western,
(c) one is a brass band, one is an opera and one is country and western music.

4   Ahmed goes to school either by car or by bicycle. If it is raining at 7.30 am in the morning, the probability of Ahmed going to school by car is 0.7. If it is not raining in the morning, the probability that he goes to school by car is 0.4. The probability of rain at 7.30 in the morning is 0.1.
A day is selected at random.

(a) Find the probability that Ahmed cycles to school.
Ahmed's teacher sees him cycling to school one morning.

(b) Find the probability that it was raining at 7.30 that morning.

(c) In a randomly chosen week of 5 days, find the probability that Ahmed only cycles into school once and goes in by car the other four times.

5   The 160 pupils at a certain village school are all registered with the school dentist. Of the 75 girls only 25 of them have seen the dentist in the past year for treatment, the others have not. However, 34 of the boys have received treatment and the rest have not. Each child's records are kept on a separate record card.

(a) A record card is selected at random. Let A represent the event that the child referred to on the card has received treatment in the past year, and the event B represent that the child referred to is a boy. Find:

(i) $P(B)$

(ii) $P(A \cap B)$

(iii) $P(A' \cap B')$

(iv) $P(B|A)$

(b) If three different record cards are selected at random without replacement, find the probability that

(i)   all three cards relate to children who have had treatment,

(ii) exactly one of the cards relates to a child who has had treatment,

(iii) one card relates to a girl who has had treatment, one to a boy who has had treatment and one to a girl who has not had treatment.

Exercise 5E   (Revision)

1 A bag A contains 4 yellow balls and 6 green balls and a
   similar bag B contains 5 yellow balls and 4 red balls. One ball
   is selected at random from A and then placed in B. One ball
   is then selected at random from B. Let Y_i, G_i and R_i, $i = 1, 2$
   represent the events that the ith ball selected is yellow, green
   or red respectively.
   (a) Show that $P(Y_1 \cap R_2) = 0.16$.
   (b) Find the probability that the second ball selected is red.
   (c) Calculate $P(G_1 | R_2)$.
   In the light of your calculations in (a), (b) and (c),
   (d) explain what can be said about the events R_2, Y_1 and G_1.

2 The three events E_1, E_2 and E_3 are defined in the same
   sample space and $P(E_1 \cup E_2 \cup E_3) = 1$. The events E_1 and E_2
   are independent. Given that $P(E_1) = \frac{2}{3}$, $P(E_2) = \frac{1}{4}$ and
   $P(E_3) = \frac{1}{4}$ find
   (a) $P(E_1 \cup E_2)$
   (b) $P(E_2 \cup E_3)$.

3 A pack of 52 playing cards is shuffled and a card is selected
   at random.
   The events R and F are defined as follows:
   R = the card is red
   F = the number on the card is 5.
   Find the following probabilities:
   (a) $P(R \cap F)$
   (b) $P(F | R)$
   (c) $P(F' | R')$.

4 The events A and B have the following probabilities
   associated with them:
   $$P(A|B) = \tfrac{1}{3}, \quad P(B|A) = \tfrac{3}{5} \quad \text{and} \quad P(B) = \tfrac{2}{5}.$$
   Find
   (a) $P(A \cap B)$ (b) $P(A)$ (c) $P(A \cup B)$.

5 Half of the 60 students in the sixth form of a certain school
   study maths. There are 11 asthma sufferers, of whom 4 study
   maths, and 8 students who wear glasses, 3 of whom also study
   maths, but no one wears glasses and suffers from asthma.

(a) Represent this information on a Venn diagram.

(b) A student is selected at random. Find the probability that the student does not study maths, does not wear glasses and does not suffer from asthma.

(c) A mathematics student is selected at random. Find the probability that the student wears glasses or suffers from asthma.

6

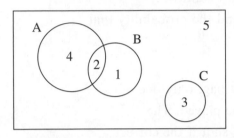

The events A, B and C are defined as in the above Venn diagram. Use the diagram to find the following probabilities:

(a) $P(A \cap B)$ (b) $P(A|B)$

(c) $P(A \cap C)$ (d) $P(A' \cup C')$.

7 Two events R and S are independent. $P(R|S) = \frac{3}{4}$ and $P(S) = P(S' \cap R')$. By letting x equal $P(S)$ and forming an equation for x, or otherwise, find

(a) $P(S)$

(b) $P(S' \cap R)$

(c) Write down $P(S|R)$.

8 I have three 2-pence pieces and two 10-pence pieces in my pocket. I pick two coins out of my pocket at random. Find the probability that they are:

(a) both 10-pence pieces,

(b) both of the same value.

(c) Find the probability that the coins are both the same, given that the first coin was a 2-pence piece.

(d) Find the probability that the first coin was a 2-pence piece given that the coins were both the same.

The event T is that the sum of the coins' values is 20 pence and the event S is that the coins are the same.

(e) Find $P(T|S)$.

(f) State, with a reason, whether or not events S and T are independent.

9 A box X contains two white balls, one blue ball and three red balls; a box Y contains four white balls, two blue balls and no red balls. An ordinary die is thrown once and, if the score is a 1 or a 6, then a ball is drawn at random from box X, otherwise a ball is drawn from box Y.

(a) Draw a tree diagram to represent this experiment.

(b) Find the probability that a white ball is drawn.

(c) Given that a white ball is drawn, find the probability that the box X is used.

10 A golfer has six different clubs in a golf bag, only one of which is correct for the shot about to be played. The probability that the golfer plays a good shot if the correct club is chosen is $\frac{2}{5}$ and the probability of a good shot with an incorrect club is $\frac{1}{3}$. The golfer chooses a club at random and plays the shot. Find the probability that

(a) a good shot is made,

(b) a correct club was used, given that a good shot is made.

(c) Comment on whether it is reasonable to suppose that the golfer chooses a club at random.

11 The security passes for a certain company are coloured yellow or white and are provided with either a clip to go on a pocket, or a chain to be worn around the neck. The probability that a pass has a clip is $\frac{6}{10}$ and $\frac{2}{3}$ of the white passes and $\frac{4}{7}$ of the yellow ones are fitted with clips. A member of the company is stopped on his way into the work and his pass checked. Find the probability that

(a) the pass is yellow,

(b) the pass is yellow with a chain.

If two people are stopped at random as they enter the company,

(c) find the probability that one pass will be yellow and the other white, and one will have a clip and the other a chain.

SUMMARY OF KEY POINTS

1
$$\text{P(event } A \text{ or event } B) = \text{P}(A \cup B)$$
$$\text{P(both events } A \text{ and } B) = \text{P}(A \cap B)$$
$$\text{P(not event } A) = \text{P}(A')$$

2 **Complementary probability**
$$\text{P}(A') = 1 - \text{P}(A)$$

3 **Addition Rule**
$$\text{P}(A \cup B) = \text{P}(A) + \text{P}(B) - \text{P}(A \cap B)$$

4 **Conditional probability**
$$\text{P}(A \text{ given } B) = \text{P}(A|B) = \frac{\text{P}(A \cap B)}{\text{P}(B)}$$

5 **Multiplication rule**
$$\text{P}(A \cap B) = \text{P}(A|B) \times \text{P}(B)$$

6 A and B are **independent** events if
$$\text{P}(A \cap B) = \text{P}(A) \times \text{P}(B)$$

7 A and B are **mutually exclusive** events if
$$\text{P}(A \cap B) = 0$$

Review exercise 1

1 John buys 10 raffle tickets and knows that he has a $\frac{1}{48}$ probability of winning the prize. How many tickets have been sold?

2 The histogram below shows the ages of members of a factory sports club.

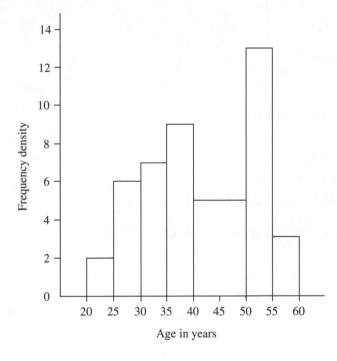

Calculate:
(a) the number of members over 50
(b) the number of members between 25 and 30
(c) the number of members in the club.

3 Two dice are tossed and the first one shows a 4. What is the probability that the second die shows an odd number?

4 A frequency distribution is shown below.

Class	1–10	11–20	21–30	31–40	41–50
Frequency	6	8	10	9	7

For this frequency distribution calculate:

(a) the semi-interquartile range

(b) the skewness.

5 All the members of a class study French or German or both.
The numbers for each are shown in the following Venn
diagram where F is the event of studying French and G is the
event of studying German.

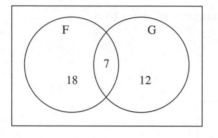

Calculate:

(a) the number of students who study French

(b) the number of students who study German

(c) how many students there are in the class.

(d) A child is chosen from the class.

Find (i) $P(F)$, (ii) $P(G)$, (iii) $P(F \cap G)$, (iv) $P(F|G)$.

6 The Venn diagram below represents the four events A, B, C
and D.

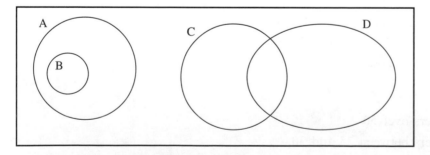

What observations can you make about:

(a) events A and C?

(b) events A and B?

(c) events C and D?

7 The stem and leaf diagram below shows the journey times to work of each of the employees of a small department store.

Journey time	2|1 means 21	Totals
1	1 1 2 4 6	( )
2	0 1 2 2 4 5 6 7	( )
3	0 1 1 2 2 4 6 8 8 8	( )
4	2 2 2 3 4	( )
5	1	( )

(a) Calculate the numbers that should go in the brackets.

(b) Calculate how many employees there are.

(c) What is the median time taken?

(d) What are the values of Q_1 and Q_3?

8 Three coins are tossed. Show that the event 'heads on the first coin' and the event 'tails on the last two' are independent. Show that the event 'exactly two coins heads' and the event 'three coins heads' are dependent.

9 The table below is the distribution of faults in very large bales of cloth.

Faults	1	2	3	4	5	6	7	8	9	10
Frequency	6	24	60	86	90	68	37	22	5	2

if a, b and σ are the mean, mode and standard deviation,

work out the value of $\dfrac{a+b}{\sigma}$ to two decimal places.

10 Find the standard deviation of the following set of numbers:

13, 17, 8, 17, 12, 6, 11, 11, 10, 5.

11 The following box plots are drawn to represent the distributions X and Y.

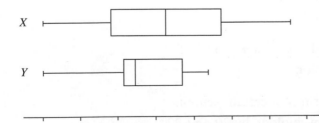

Make two statements that compare them in some way.

12 The number of breakdowns per week were recorded over a 32 week period by a rail company. They were as follows:

$$3\ 3\ 3\ 1\ 3\ 2\ 4\ 6$$
$$6\ 3\ 1\ 4\ 3\ 4\ 3\ 3$$
$$0\ 4\ 3\ 3\ 5\ 2\ 3\ 4$$
$$3\ 3\ 4\ 5\ 2\ 3\ 4\ 2$$

Make a frequency table of the distribution and find the mean and median number of breakdowns together with the standard deviation of the distribution.

13 A box contains 15 bags of sweets. Eight bags contain chocolates and 7 contain mints. If a bag is selected at random from the box, what is the probability that it contains chocolates?

14 The following Venn diagram represents all the members of a dancing school.
B is the event of studying ballet,
T is the event of studying tap, and
G is the event of studying Greek dance.

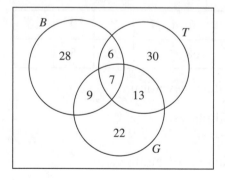

(a) How many dance members are there in the school?
(b) What is the probability that any member chosen at random studies
(i) all three subjects, (ii) ballet and tap,
(iii) tap given that they already study Greek?

15 Give one advantage of using a back-to-back stem and leaf diagram when studying two distributions.

16 There are 60 students in the sixth form of a certain school. Mathematics is studied by 27 of them, biology by 20 and 22 students study neither mathematics nor biology,

(a) Find the probability that a randomly selected student studies both mathematics and biology.

(b) Find the probability that a randomly selected mathematics student does not study biology.

A student is selected at random.

(c) Determine whether the event 'studying mathematics' is statistically independent of the event 'not studying biology'.

[E]

17   The average weekly incomes, in £, of households in 11 regions of the United Kingdom are given below:

$$255.8, \ 252.0, \ 270.6, \ 298.4, \ 362.3, \ 297.2,$$
$$266.8, \ 261.7, \ 247.5, \ 259.1, \ 220.6$$

(a) Find the median and upper and lower quartiles.

(b) On graph paper, draw a box and whisker plot to represent these data.

(c) Identify a possible outlier.

(d) Calculate the mean and standard deviation for these data. Further investigations suggested that the £362.30 value could be incorrect and should in fact be £326.30.

(e) Without carrying out any further calculations indicate what effect this change would have on

(i)   the standard deviation,

(ii) the interquartile range.   [E]

18   A golfer has five different clubs in a golf bag, only one of which is correct for the shot about to be played. The probability that the golfer plays a good shot if the correct club is chosen is one third and the probability of a good shot with an incorrect club is one quarter. The golfer chooses a club at random and plays the shot. Find the probability that

(a) a good shot is made,

(b) an incorrect club was used, given that a good shot is played.

Comment on whether it is reasonable to suppose that the golfer chooses a club at random.   [E]

19   A consumer group is investigating telephone usage within a particular city. The numbers of telephone units, x, used in a

particular quarter by a random sample of 250 households were summarised in a group frequency table. In order to simplify the arithmetic the data in the table were coded such that

$$y = \frac{x - 290}{10} \quad \text{gving} \quad \sum fy = -40 \quad \text{and} \quad \sum fy^2 = 1075$$

(a) Find estimates of the mean and the variance of the number of telephone units used in that quarter by households in the city.

(b) Suggest two ways in which the estimates in (a) might be improved. [E]

20 Summarised below are the data relating to the number of minutes, to the nearest minute, that a random sample of 65 trains from Darlingborough were late arriving at a main line station.

Minutes late	0|2 means 2	Totals
0	2 3 3 3 4 4 4 4 5 5 5 5 5 5	(14)
0	6 6 6 7 7 8 8 8 9	(9)
1	0 0 0 2 2 3 3 4 4 4 5	( )
1	6 6 7 7 8 8 8 9 9	( )
2	1 2 2 3 3 3 3 4	( )
2	6	( )
3	3 4 4 5	(4)
3	6 8	(2)
4	1 3	(2)
4	7 7 9	(3)
5	2 4	(2)

(a) Write down the values needed to complete the stem and leaf diagram.

(b) Find the median and the quartiles of these times.

(c) Find the 67th percentile.

(d) On graph paper construct a box plot for these data, showing clearly your scale.

A random sample of trains arriving at the same main line station from Shefton had a minimum value of 15 minutes late and a maximum of 30 minutes. The quartiles were 18, 22 and 27 minutes.

(e) On the same graph paper and using the same scale, construct a box plot for these data.

(f) Compare and contrast the journeys from Darlingborough and Shefton based on these data. [E]

21 In a large garden there are 7 fruit trees and 13 other types of tree. Six of the trees have birds nesting in them but only 2 of these are fruit trees.

(a) Copy and complete the table below to illustrate this information.

	Fruit tree	*Other tree*	*Total*
Birds nest	2		6
No nest			
Total	7	13	

The owner of the garden has given permission for Abdul to play in the garden but has instructed him not to climb any of the fruit trees that have birds nesting in them. Abdul selects a tree at random to climb.

(b) Find the probability that Abdul will obey the owner's instructions.

Given that Abdul climbs a fruit tree,

(c) find the probability that the tree has birds nesting in it.   [E]

22 At a children's party each child was blindfolded and asked to pin a tail on a cardboard donkey. The distance, in cm, of the pin from the correct position was measured and the results are recorded below.

$$17, \ 15, \ 5, \ 9, \ 13, \ 42, \ 8, \ 24, \ 34, \ 38, \ 29, \ 6$$

Find the mean and the standard deviation for this set of numbers.   [E]

23 In a certain cross-country running competition the times that each of the 136 runners took to complete the course were recorded to the nearest minute. The winner completed the course in 23 minutes and the final runner came in with a time of 78 minutes. The full results are summarised in the table below.

Recorded time	20–29	30–39	40–49	50–59	60–69	70–79
Frequency	7	21	42	37	20	9

On graph paper draw a box plot for the results from this competition. You should mark the end points, the median and the quartiles clearly on your diagram.   [E]

24 The three events E_1, E_2 and E_3 are defined in the same
sample space. The events E_1 and E_3 are mutually exclusive.
The events E_1 and E_2 are independent.
Given that $P(E_1) = \frac{2}{5}$, $P(E_3) = \frac{1}{3}$ and $P(E_1 \cup E_2) = \frac{5}{8}$, find
(a) $P(E_1 \cup E_3)$
(b) $P(E_2)$. [E]

25 The following stem and leaf diagram summarises the blood
glucose level, in mmol/l, of a patient, measured daily over a
period of time.

Blood glucose level	5|0 means 5.0	Totals
5	0 0 1 1 1 2 2 3 3 3 4 4	(12)
5	5 5 6 6 7 8 8 9 9	(9)
6	0 1 1 1 2 3 4 4 4 4	(10)
6	5 5 6 7 8 9 9	( )
7	1 1 2 2 2 3	( )
7	5 7 9 9	( )
8	1 1 1 2 2 3 3 4	( )
8	7 9 9	(3)
9	0 1 1 2	(4)
9	5 7 9	(3)

(a) Write down the numbers required to complete the stem
and leaf diagram.
(b) Find the median and quartiles of these data.
(c) On graph paper, construct a box plot to represent these
data. Show your scale clearly. [E]

26 The following figures show the number of goals scored during
a tournament by sixty hockey clubs:

$$0\ 4\ 6\ 3\ 4\ 5\ 1\ 3\ 2\ 4$$
$$4\ 1\ 3\ 5\ 5\ 6\ 2\ 4\ 7\ 6$$
$$3\ 6\ 7\ 0\ 1\ 7\ 4\ 1\ 5\ 3$$
$$5\ 8\ 3\ 2\ 6\ 2\ 6\ 6\ 7\ 7$$
$$3\ 5\ 2\ 5\ 5\ 3\ 8\ 4\ 6\ 4$$
$$4\ 7\ 7\ 4\ 4\ 8\ 4\ 3\ 5\ 2$$

Construct a frequency distribution for these data.

27 The mean height of a sample of 15 boys is 1.38 m and the
mean height of a sample of 20 girls is 1.22 m. Find the mean
height of the combined sample of boys and girls. [E]

28 The stalk lengths (pedicels) of creeping buttercup were
measured. These are the results.

Pedicel length (mm)	Frequency
1–20	32
21–30	63
31–40	52
41–55	44
56–70	28
71–90	13
Total	232

Draw a histogram to illustrate these data.

29 The probability that a door-to-door salesman convinces a
customer to buy is 0.7. Assuming sales are independent find
the probability that the salesman makes a sale before reaching
the fourth house. [E]

30 Show that for any two events E and F:
$$P(E \cup F) = P(E) + P(F) - P(E \cap F).$$
Express in words the meaning of $P(E|F)$. [E]

31 The grouped frequency distribution of the weights of 40
university students is as follows:

Weight (kg)	53–56	57–60	61–64	65–68	69–72	73–76	77–80
Frequency	2	3	4	11	9	6	5

Determine:
(a) the lower class boundary of the third class
(b) the upper class boundary of the fourth class
(c) the class width of the second class
(d) the lower class limit of the seventh class
(e) the class mid-point of the seventh class.

32 Classes of students, from three different schools, sat the same
examination paper. The mean scores for each school were 63,
48 and 72 per cent. If the respective class sizes were 23,
30 and 15 students, find the mean mark for the three schools
taken together.

33 When a person needs a minicab, she hires it from one of three firms X, Y and Z. Of her hirings 40% are from X, 50% are from Y and 10% are from Z. For cabs hired from X, 9% arrive late, the corresponding percentages for cabs hired from firms Y and Z being 6% and 20% respectively.

Calculate the probability that the next cab she hires:

(a) will be from X and will not arrive late

(b) will arrive late.

Given that she calls for a minicab and that it arrives late, find, to 3 decimal places, the probability that it came from Y.

[E]

34 A dairy farm records the milk yield, in litres, for each of its herd of 40 pedigree friesian cows. For one particular day the yields were as follows:

```
26  40  34  39  35  23  15  35  32  13
37  11  26  12  23  37  35  39  41  33
 5  34  25   5   7  42  19  41  36  12
34  25  39  23  29  24  36  25  39  33
```

Construct a stem and leaf diagram to represent these data.
Find the median value.

35 In a series of Intelligence Tests, 40 adults between the ages of sixty and seventy-five were each given two different tests [AH1 and AH2]. The results were as shown.

AH1					AH2				
34	32	48	42	41	25	34	40	28	45
16	37	30	44	41	16	18	29	24	25
59	62	12	36	24	34	18	32	25	51
50	44	56	18	44	19	40	9	44	14
47	23	34	40	41	26	50	18	23	36
50	21	40	25	25	34	10	16	23	17
34	23	26	32	37	26	31	38	19	23
34	28	54	30	30	22	44	17	34	37

Compare these data by constructing a back-to-back stem and leaf diagram. Comment on your results.

36 A marketing company always buys new cars on 1st August. Before making any purchases on 1st August 1994, they reviewed their fleet of cars. The following table shows the age, x, in years, of the cars in the fleet:

Age (x)	1	2	3	4	5	6	7	8	9	10	11
Number of cars (f)	14	20	16	14	12	8	6	4	3	2	1

Find:

(a) the mode

(b) the median and the quartiles

(c) the mean of this distribution.

Draw a box plot to represent these data. Comment on the shape of your box plot. [E]

37 Cartons of orange are filled by a machine. A sample of 10 cartons selected at random from the production contained the following quantities of orange (in ml).

        201.2   205.0   209.1   202.3   204.6

        206.4   210.1   201.9   203.7   207.3

Calculate estimates of the mean and variance of the population from which this sample was taken. [E]

38 Define, in words or in symbols, the meaning of each of the following statements.

(a) Two events E and F are independent.

(b) Two events G and H are mutually exclusive.

Three events A, B and C are defined in the same sample space. The events A and C are mutually exclusive. The events A and B are independent. Given that:

$$P(A) = \tfrac{1}{3}, \ P(C) = \tfrac{1}{5}, \ P(A \cup B) = \tfrac{2}{3}$$

find:

$$P(A \cup C), \ P(B), \ P(A \cap B).$$

Given also that $P(B \cup C) = \tfrac{3}{5}$, determine whether or not B and C are independent. [E]

39 The following table shows the time, to the nearest minute, spent writing during a particular day by a group of school children.

Time	Number of children
10–19	10
20–24	20
25–29	25
30–39	30
40–49	24
50–64	12
65–89	10

(a) Represent these data by a histogram.

(b) Comment on the shape of the distribution.   [E]

40 The table below summarizes data taken from the results of a promotion examination taken by 310 police constables.

Range of marks	0–9	10–19	20–29	30–39	40–49	50–59	60–69	70–79	80–100
Number of candidates	1	4	19	90	64	61	56	14	1

By calculation estimate:

(a) the median and upper and lower quartiles

(b) D_4 and D_7

(c) P_5 and P_{95}.

41 In a certain town an investigation was carried out into accidents in the home to children under 12 years of age. The numbers of reported accidents and the ages of the children concerned are summarised below:

Group	A	B	C	D	E	F
Age of child (years)	0 to < 2	2 to < 4	4 to < 6	6 to < 8	8 to < 10	10 to < 12
Number of accidents	42	52	28	20	18	16

(a) State the modal class.

(b) Calculate, to the nearest month, the mean age and the standard deviation of the distribution of ages.

42 Given that E and F are independent events, $P(E) = \frac{1}{5}$ and $P(E \cap F) = \frac{1}{30}$, find $P(E|F)$, $P(F)$ and $P(E \cup F)$.

43 Two coins are to be tossed one after the other. Find the
probability that exactly one will show a head.
Let E denote the event that 'the first coin shows a head' and
F denote the event that 'exactly one coin shows a head'.
Investigate the independence of the two events E and F.

44 The table below summarises data relating to the lifetime of a
random sample of 200 bulbs taken from the production line
of a particular manufacturer.

Lifetime (to nearest hour)	Number of bulbs
700–719	10
720–729	14
730–739	16
740–749	21
750–754	35
755–759	41
760–764	38
765–769	15
770–779	7
780–799	3

(a) By calculation, estimate the median and quartiles of these
lifetimes. Give your answers to 1 decimal place.

(b) One method of assessing the skewness of a distribution is
to calculate

$$\frac{3\,(\text{mean} - \text{median})}{\text{standard deviation}}$$

Evaluate this, to 1 decimal place, for the above distribution.

(c) Use the quartiles to assess skewness and state whether or not
you feel this result is compatible with your answer to (b).   [E]

45 In a borehole the thicknesses, in mm, of the 25 strata are as
shown in the table below:

Thicknesses of borehole strata

Thickness (mm)	0–	20–	30–	40–	50–	60–
Number of strata	2	5	9	8	1	0

Draw a histogram to illustrate these data. Estimate the
median and the interquartile range for these data.   [E]

46 A sample of students sitting an entrance examination for the civil service has the following distribution of verbal reasoning (V.R.) scores.

V.R. score	80–99	100–109	110–119	120–129	130–139	140–149
Frequency	17	50	250	120	55	8

Calculate the mean and standard deviation of this distribution.

47 A random sample of 51 people were asked to record the number of miles they travelled by car in a given week. The distances, to the nearest mile, are shown below.

```
67  76  85  42  93  48  93  46
52  72  77  53  41  48  86  78
56  80  70  70  66  62  54  85
60  58  43  58  74  44  52  74
52  82  78  47  66  50  67  87
78  86  94  63  72  63  44  47
57  68  81
```

(a) Construct a stem and leaf diagram to represent these data.
(b) Find the median and the quartiles of this distribution.
(c) Draw a box plot to represent these data.
Give one advantage of using (i) a stem and leaf diagram,
(ii) a box plot, to illustrate data such as that given above. [E]

48 A box of matches should contain 50 matches. A quality control department set up a test to check that the contents were satisfactory. A sample of 50 matchboxes gave the following results for the variable x, the number of matches in a box:

$$\sum x = 2514 \quad \text{and} \quad \sum x^2 = 126\,486$$

Estimate the mean and standard deviation of the number of matches in a box.

49 A railway enthusiast simulates train journeys and records the number of minutes, x, to the nearest minute, trains are late according to the schedule being used. A random sample of 50 journeys gave the times listed at the top of the next page.

17	5	3	10	4	3	10	5	2	14
3	14	5	5	21	9	22	36	14	34
22	4	23	6	8	15	41	23	13	7
6	13	33	8	5	34	26	17	8	43
24	14	23	4	19	5	23	13	12	10

(a) Construct a stem and leaf diagram to represent these data.

(b) Comment on the shape of the distribution produced by your diagram.

(c) Given that $\sum x = 738$ and $\sum x^2 = 16\,526$, calculate to 2 decimal places estimates of the mean and the variance of the population from which this sample was drawn.

(d) Explain briefly the effect that grouping of these data would have had on your calculations in (c).   [E]

50 The following grouped frequency distribution summarises the values of orders taken by sales representatives employed by a company during one particular year.

Value of order (£)	Number of orders
0–	80
10–	120
20–	226
30–	135
50–	105
100–	40
150–	24
200–	12
500–	8
1000–	0

Let X represent the mid-point of each group.

(a) Using the coding $U = \dfrac{X - 25}{5}$ show that $\sum fu = 4355$, where f represents the frequency in each group. Estimate the mean and standard deviation of the value of the orders.
(You may use $\sum fu^2 = 269\,975$.)

(b) Explain why these two measures might not be the best ones to use when analysing these data.

(c) Which alternative measures of location and spread would you recommend?   [E]

Correlation

6

6.1 Correlation

There are many situations where we are interested in the association between two random variables such as the height and weight of people, or the mark a person attained in Mathematics and the mark they attained in Physics. Pairs of observations of two such variables produce a **bi-variate distribution**.

While you might expect there to be a relationship between Mathematics and Physics marks, you cannot necessarily expect to find a law relating them. You can only look initially for the most basic of associations, such as:

Does a higher than average Mathematics mark usually go with a higher than average Physics mark, or does a higher than average Mathematics mark go with a lower than average Physics mark?

The technique used to measure the degree of linear association between two variables is called **linear correlation**. If both variables increase together we say that they are **positively correlated**. For example, height and weight of people might be positively correlated. If one variable increases as the other decreases then they are said to be **negatively correlated**. For example, the number of goals conceded by a team and their position in the league might be negatively correlated. If no pattern can be seen then there is said to be no correlation between the variables. For example, there is no correlation between a person's height and the amount they earn.

6.2 Scatter diagrams

The association between two variables may be seen by plotting pairs of observations of the variables on a graph. Such a graph is known as a **scatter diagram** since it enables you to see how the pairs of points are scattered.

These scatter diagrams show possible associations:

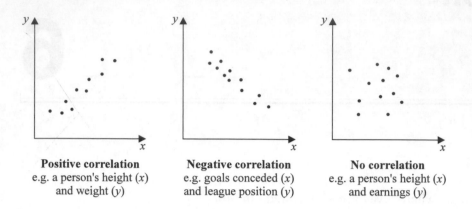

Positive correlation
e.g. a person's height (x)
and weight (y)

Negative correlation
e.g. goals conceded (x)
and league position (y)

No correlation
e.g. a person's height (x)
and earnings (y)

When drawing these graphs you could have plotted x vertically and y horizontally without affecting their association.

If a horizontal line is drawn through the mean y value, $\bar{y}$, and a vertical line through the mean x value, $\bar{x}$, and if you move the axes to these two lines, you can see the association between the two variables in another way.

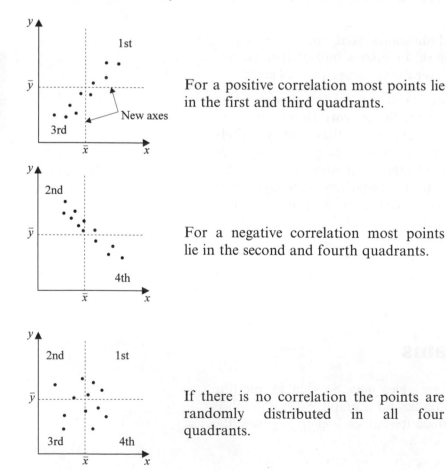

For a positive correlation most points lie in the first and third quadrants.

For a negative correlation most points lie in the second and fourth quadrants.

If there is no correlation the points are randomly distributed in all four quadrants.

Example 1

The weights (kg), head sizes (circumference in cm) and gestation periods (weeks) of new-born male babies at a certain clinic over a period of time were as follows.

Baby	A	B	C	D	E	F	G	H	I	J
Weight w (kg)	3.10	3.24	3.15	3.30	3.12	3.41	3.52	3.40	3.53	3.74
Head size h (cm)	31.1	33.3	30.0	31.5	35.0	30.2	36.4	37.3	31.4	34.0
Gestation period p (weeks)	36	37	38	38	40	40	40	41	41	41

It is suggested that head size h and weight w may be correlated, and that the gestation period p and weight w might also be correlated.

Plot scatter diagrams and state whether there is evidence to support this suggestion. If there is, state whether the correlation is positive or negative. (You may use $\bar{w} = 3.35$, $\bar{h} = 33.02$, $\bar{p} = 39.2$.)

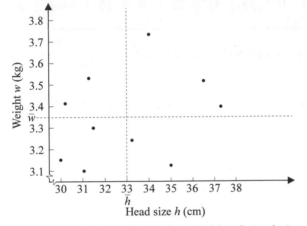

Scatter diagram of weight w (kg) and head size h (cm)

Points are fairly evenly scattered in all four quadrants so there is no evidence of a correlation between head size h and weight w.

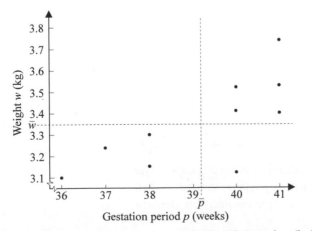

Scatter diagram of gestation period p (weeks) and w (kg)

Since most of the points of the scatter diagram lie in the first and third quadrants there is evidence of a positive correlation between weight w and gestation period p. As the gestation period increases the weight increases.

Example 2

In the study of a city, the population density p (people/hectare), and the distance from the city centre d (km) was investigated by selecting a number of sample areas at random, with the following results.

Area	A	B	C	D	E	F	G	H	I	J
Distance, d (km)	0.6	3.8	2.4	3.0	2.0	1.5	1.8	3.4	4.0	0.9
Population density, p (people/hectare)	50	22	14	20	33	47	25	8	16	38

Plot a scatter diagram and by plotting the mean values of d and p suggest what type of correlation is present.

$$\bar{d} = \frac{\Sigma d}{n} = 2.34$$

$$\bar{p} = \frac{\Sigma p}{n} = 27.3$$

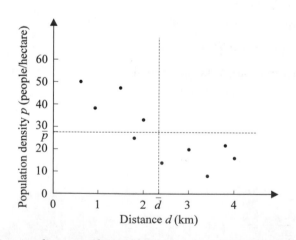

Scatter diagram of population density p and distance d

Most points lie in the second and fourth quadrants, so the population density p and distance from the city centre d are negatively correlated. As distance increases the population density decreases.

6.3 Product-moment correlation coefficient (PMCC)

You can see from a scatter diagram whether two variables are correlated, but you have no measure of the strength of this correlation. The diagram below shows a typical scatter diagram for n pairs of observations of the two variables x and y.

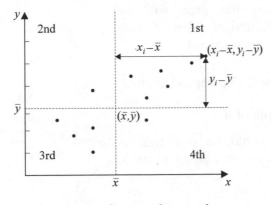

Scatter diagram for x and y

To show up any relationship more clearly, you can move the origin of the diagram to the point $(\bar{x}, \bar{y})$. The coordinate of a typical point (x_i, y_i) will now be written as $(x_i - \bar{x}, y_i - \bar{y})$. The ith point on the diagram has been labelled to show this.

If you look at the scatter diagram you can see the signs ($+$ or $-$) taken by all the $x_i - \bar{x}$ and $y_i - \bar{y}$ in the four new quadrants. By multiplying the signs, you can find the sign taken by their product $(x_i - \bar{x})(y_i - \bar{y})$.

Quadrant	$x_i - \bar{x}$	$y_i - \bar{y}$	$(x_i - \bar{x})(y_i - \bar{y})$
first	+	+	+
second	−	+	−
third	−	−	+
fourth	+	−	−

Now think about the three types of correlation:

If there is a **positive correlation**, most points lie in the first and third quadrants so $\Sigma(x_i - \bar{x})(y_i - \bar{y})$ **would be positive**.

If there is a **negative correlation**, most points lie in the second and fourth quadrants so $\Sigma(x_i - \bar{x})(y_i - \bar{y})$ **would be negative**.

If there is **no correlation** the points lie in all four quadrants and $\Sigma(x_i - \bar{x})(y_i - \bar{y})$ **is zero or close to zero**, since the positive and negative values tend to cancel out.

You can now see why we call a correlation positive or negative.

The numerical value of $\Sigma(x_i - \bar{x})(y_i - \bar{y})$ will depend on the units of measurement. To see this, think about a simple calculation of area. If you measure the area of a rectangle 10 mm by 12 mm in square millimetres the area will be $10 \times 12 = 120 \, \text{mm}^2$. If you measure the same shape in centimetres the area will be $1 \times 1.2 = 1.2 \, \text{cm}^2$. In the same way the numerical value of each $(x_i - \bar{x})(y_i - \bar{y})$ will depend on the units of measurement.

The numerical value of $\sum_{i=1}^{n}(x_i - \bar{x})(y_i - \bar{y})$ will also depend on how many values are added together, i.e. the value of n.

A more useful measure of correlation would be one that is independent of the sample size and the scales of measurement used.

This is achieved by dividing by $\sqrt{\sum(x_i - \bar{x})^2} \sqrt{\sum(y_i - \bar{y})^2}$ to give

$$\frac{\sum(x_i - \bar{x})(y_i - \bar{y})}{\sqrt{(x_i - \bar{x})^2} \sqrt{(y_i - \bar{y})^2}}$$

This measure is known as the **product-moment correlation coefficient** r. Although its derivation is beyond the scope of this book you will need to know the formula for r and be able to use it.

■ $$r = \frac{\sum(x_i - \bar{x})(y_i - \bar{y})}{\sqrt{\left(\sum(x_i - \bar{x})^2\right)} \sqrt{\sum(y_i - \bar{y})^2}}$$

For short, we normally denote $\sum(x_i - \bar{x})(y_i - \bar{y})$ by S_{xy}. So:

■ $$S_{xy} = \sum(x_i - \bar{x})(y_i - \bar{y})$$

and in a similar way we write:

■ $$S_{xx} = \sum(x_i - \bar{x})^2$$

and

■ $$S_{yy} = \sum(y_i - \bar{y})^2$$

■ **Product-moment correlation coefficient**

$$r = \frac{S_{xy}}{\sqrt{(S_{xx}S_{yy})}}$$

Summations of the form $\sum(x_i - \bar{x})^p(y_i - \bar{y})^q$ are known as product-moments about the mean. The one we are interested in is of low order, with $p = q = 1$. (The others will not be of concern to you.) But this explains why the standardised measure is called the product-moment correlation coefficient. Because of the standardisation, the measure can be shown to lie in the interval -1 to $+1$, and it gives us a measure of the strength of the association between the two variables.

Example 3

The mean points scored in the GCSE and the mean points scored at A-level by pupils of a sample of schools from a particular county were:

School	A	B	C	D	E	F	G	H	I	J	K	L	M	N	O
A-level (x)	8.6	13.4	12.8	9.3	1.3	9.4	13.1	4.9	13.5	9.6	7.5	9.8	23.3	21	19.4
GCSE (y)	33	51	30	48	12	23	46	18	36	50	34	35	95	99	69

(a) Draw a scatter diagram of these results.

(b) Calculate the product-moment correlation coefficient for GCSE and A-level scores.

(a)

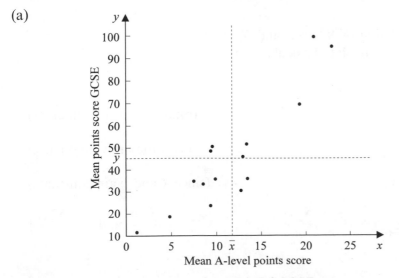

Scatter diagram of A-level and GCSE points

(b) The mean values of x and y are:
$$\bar{y} = 45.27 \qquad \bar{x} = 11.80$$

x	y	$x - \bar{x}$	$y - \bar{y}$	$(x - \bar{x})^2$	$(y - \bar{y})^2$	$(x - \bar{x})(y - \bar{y})$
8.6	33	−3.2	−12.27	10.24	150.55	39.26
13.4	51	1.6	5.73	2.56	32.83	9.17
12.8	30	1	−15.27	1.00	233.17	−15.27
9.3	48	−2.5	2.73	6.25	7.45	−6.83
1.3	12	−10.5	−33.27	110.25	1106.89	349.34
9.4	23	−2.4	−22.27	5.76	495.95	53.45
13.1	46	1.3	0.73	1.69	0.53	0.95
4.9	18	−6.9	−27.27	47.61	743.65	188.16
13.5	36	1.7	−9.27	2.89	85.93	−15.76
9.6	50	−2.2	4.73	4.84	22.37	−10.41
7.5	34	−4.3	−11.27	18.49	127.01	48.46
9.8	35	−2	−10.27	4.00	105.47	20.54
23.3	95	11.5	49.73	132.25	2473.07	571.90
21.0	99	9.2	53.73	84.64	2886.91	494.32
19.4	69	7.6	23.73	57.76	563.11	180.35
				$S_{xx} = 490.23$	$S_{yy} = 9034.89$	$S_{xy} = 1907.63$

The product-moment correlation coefficient is:

$$r = \frac{S_{xy}}{\sqrt{(S_{xx}S_{yy})}} = \frac{\sum(x_i - \bar{x})(y_i - \bar{y})}{\sqrt{\sum(x_i - \bar{x})^2(y_i - \bar{y})^2}}$$

$$= \frac{1907.63}{\sqrt{(490.23 \times 9034.89)}}$$

$$= 0.906$$

A quicker way of finding the product-moment correlation coefficient r

By means of some algebraic manipulation of S_{xy}, S_{xx} and S_{yy} you can find another formula that can save you a lot of calculation time.

$$S_{xy} = \sum(x_i - \bar{x})(y_i - \bar{y})$$

$$= \sum(x_i y_i - \bar{x}y_i - \bar{y}x_i + \bar{x}\bar{y}) \qquad \text{(multiply out the brackets)}$$

$$= \sum x_i y_i - \sum \bar{x}y_i - \sum \bar{y}x_i + \sum \bar{x}\bar{y} \qquad \text{(sum the individual parts)}$$

$$= \sum x_i y_i - \bar{x}\sum y_i - \bar{y}\sum x_i + n\bar{x}\bar{y} \qquad \text{(since } \bar{x} \text{ and } \bar{y} \text{ are constants)}$$

$$= \sum x_i y_i - \frac{\sum x_i}{n}\sum y_i - \frac{\sum y_i}{n}\sum x_i + n\frac{\sum x_i}{n}\frac{\sum y_i}{n} \qquad \left(\bar{x} = \frac{\sum x_i}{n} \text{ and } \bar{y} = \frac{\sum y_i}{n}\right)$$

$$= \sum x_i y_i - \frac{\sum x_i \sum y_i}{n}$$

If you treat S_{xx} and S_{yy} in a similar way you get:

$$S_{xx} = \sum x_i^2 - \frac{(\sum x_i)^2}{n}$$

$$S_{yy} = \sum y_i^2 - \frac{(\sum y_i)^2}{n}$$

You do not have to be able to derive these formulae but you need to be able to use them in the product-moment correlation coefficient calculations, as it saves time. Both forms are given in the Edexcel booklet of mathematical formulae. Using these gives:

■ $r = \dfrac{S_{xy}}{\sqrt{(S_{xx}S_{yy})}}$

■ $r = \dfrac{\sum x_i y_i - \dfrac{\sum x_i \sum y_i}{n}}{\sqrt{\left[\left(\sum x_i^2 - \dfrac{(\sum x_i)^2}{n}\right)\left(\sum y_i^2 - \dfrac{(\sum y_i)^2}{n}\right)\right]}}$

It is also possible to obtain statistical calculators which, when you feed in the pairs of values, do all the calculations for you and give a value for r. If you have one of these you can check that you can use your calculator correctly by doing example 3.

Example 4
Using the figures from example 3 calculate the PMCC using the formula more suited to calculation.

x	y	x^2	y^2	xy
8.6	33	73.96	1809	283.8
13.4	51	179.56	2601	683.4
12.8	30	163.84	900	384
9.3	48	86.49	2304	446.4
1.3	12	1.69	144	15.6
9.4	23	88.36	529	216.2
13.1	46	171.61	2116	602.6
4.9	18	24.01	324	88.2
13.5	36	182.25	1296	486
9.6	50	92.16	2500	480
7.5	34	56.25	1156	255
9.8	35	96.04	1225	343
23.3	95	542.89	9025	2213.5
21	99	441	9801	2079
19.4	69	376.36	4761	1338.6
$\sum x = 176.9$	$\sum y = 679$	$\sum x^2 = 2576.47$	$\sum y^2 = 39\,771$	$\sum xy = 9915.3$

$$r = \frac{S_{xy}}{\sqrt{(S_{xx}S_{yy})}} = \frac{\sum x_i y_i - \dfrac{\sum x_i \sum y_i}{n}}{\sqrt{\left[\left(\sum x_i^2 - \dfrac{(\sum x_i)^2}{n}\right)\left(\sum y_i^2 - \dfrac{(\sum y_i)^2}{n}\right)\right]}}$$

$$= \frac{9915.3 - \dfrac{176.9 \times 679}{15}}{\sqrt{\left[\left(2576.47 - \dfrac{176.9^2}{15}\right)\left(39\,771 - \dfrac{679^2}{15}\right)\right]}}$$

$$= \frac{1907.63}{\sqrt{(490.23 \times 9034.93)}}$$

$$= 0.906\ldots$$

If you use a statistical calculator it may give you the value of the product-moment correlation coefficient. To just write down the answer is risky since no marks will be given if it is incorrect. It is also possible that you may be asked to find intermediate values in the calculation such as S_{xx}, S_{yy}, etc., as well as the value of r. It is not necessary to draw up a table. A good layout for the above question might be as follows:

$$\sum x = 176.9 \quad \sum y = 679 \quad \sum x^2 = 2576.47 \quad \sum y^2 = 39\,771$$

$$\sum xy = 9915.3$$

$$S_{xx} = 2576.47 - \frac{176.9^2}{15} = 490.23$$

$$S_{yy} = 39\,771 - \frac{679^2}{15} = 9034.93$$

$$S_{xy} = 9915.3 - \frac{176.9 \times 679}{15} = 1907.63$$

$$r = \frac{S_{xy}}{\sqrt{(S_{xx}S_{yy})}} = \frac{1907.63}{\sqrt{(490.23 \times 9034.93)}}$$

$$r = 0.906\ldots$$

Using a method of coding

You can further simplify the calculations by making the numbers you use for the values of x and y smaller. You can subtract any number from the x values, since this only moves the axis. You can divide the result by any number, since this only changes the scale. The correlation coefficient is unaffected by either of these operations. The number you subtract and divide by can be selected in any way you choose, but it is common sense to make their values such that the resulting numbers are small. You can rewrite the variables x and y as

$$X = \frac{x - a}{b} \quad \text{and} \quad Y = \frac{y - c}{d}$$

where a, b, c and d are suitable numbers to be chosen. The next example illustrates this method.

Example 5

Use the method of coding to find the product-moment correlation coefficient for x and y if the values of x and y are as shown in the table below. Draw a scatter diagram of the new values.

x	1020	1032	1028	1034	1023	1038
y	320	335	345	355	360	380

You can use the coding:

$$X = \frac{x - 1020}{1} \qquad Y = \frac{y - 300}{5}$$

Here $a = 1020$ and $b = 1$. These were chosen because 1020 was the smallest x value and the numbers then left had no common divisor. In the same way $c = 300$ and $d = 5$ since the numbers that are left have 5 as a common divisor. (We could have used 320 and made the values even smaller, but wished to show that *any* number will do the job.)

Here is the scatter diagram of the new values:

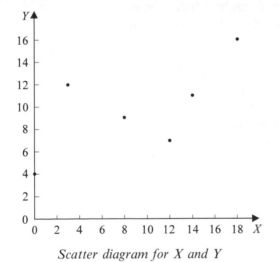

Scatter diagram for X and Y

X	Y	X^2	Y^2	XY
0	4	0	16	0
12	7	144	49	84
8	9	64	81	72
14	11	196	121	154
3	12	9	144	36
18	16	324	256	288
$\sum X = 55$	$\sum Y = 59$	$\sum X^2 = 737$	$\sum Y^2 = 667$	$\sum XY = 634$

$$r = \frac{S_{xy}}{\sqrt{(S_{xx}S_{yy})}} = \frac{\sum X_i Y_i - \dfrac{\sum X_i \sum Y_i}{n}}{\sqrt{\left[\left(\sum X_i^2 - \dfrac{(\sum X_i)^2}{n}\right)\left(\sum Y_i^2 - \dfrac{(\sum Y_i)^2}{n}\right)\right]}}$$

$$= \frac{634 - \dfrac{55 \times 59}{6}}{\sqrt{\left[\left(737 - \dfrac{55^2}{6}\right)\left(667 - \dfrac{59^2}{6}\right)\right]}}$$

$$= \frac{93.17}{142.19}$$

$$= 0.655$$

6.4 Interpreting the product-moment correlation coefficient

In examples 3 and 4 we found the value of the product-moment coefficient by using two different formulae. But what does a value of r actually tell you?

For values of r between 0 and 1, the nearer the value of r is to 1 the stronger the positive correlation between the two variables. If you look at example 3 you can see what a strong positive correlation ($r = 0.906$) looks like on a scatter diagram. In example 5 ($r = 0.6555$) you can see what a weaker one looks like.

For values between -1 and 0, the closer the value of r gets to -1 the stronger the negative correlation.

It is always a good idea to plot a scatter diagram, as this gives you a picture of the correlation, and also helps to identify any results that are well away from the other points and so do not fit the general pattern of any correlation shown up by the diagram. These are known as **rogue results**. A rogue result may sometimes be called an **outlier** and may have occurred in a number of ways – for example, a value may have been misread or a child was ill during a test and underperformed thus upsetting the general trend. A detailed study of this topic is beyond the scope of this book; it is dealt with in Book S3.

■ **If $r = 1$ there is a perfect positive linear correlation between the two variables (all points fit a straight line with positive gradient).**

■ If $r = -1$ there is a perfect negative linear correlation between the two variables (all points fit a straight line with negative gradient).

■ If r is zero (or close to zero) there is no linear correlation; this does not, however, exclude any other sort of relationship.

These cases are illustrated below:

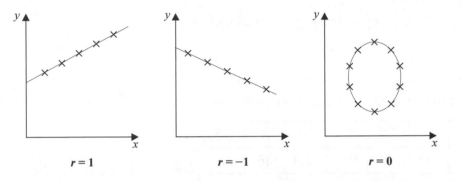

Because two variables have a linear correlation (positive or negative) it does not necessarily mean they are related. For example, there may be a correlation between the number of cars on the road and the number of television sets bought, but this does not mean that the two are related. So you should have some reason to believe that there might be a relationship before calculating the product-moment correlation coefficient, unless your aim is to prove that they are unrelated.

Often variables are linked only through a third variable. A good example of this is changes that take place over time. For example, over the past ten years the memory capacity of personal computers has increased, and so has the average life expectancy of people in the western world. The two are not connected, but both are due to scientific development over time.

Exercise 6A

1 Which of the following product-moment correlation coefficients shows   (a) the least correlation?
(b) the most correlation?
      (i) -0.99 (ii) -0.32 (iii) 0.00 (iv) 0.56

2 Two variables have a negative linear correlation. Between what values must the product-moment correlation coefficient lie?

3 Which of the following product-moment correlation coefficients express   (i) perfect correlation,   (ii) no correlation?
$-0.45, 1.00, 0.61, -0.99, 0.00, 0.83, 0.99, -1.00, 0.01$

4 Find the product-moment correlation coefficient for each of the following sets of data.

(a) $\sum x_i = 367$, $\sum y_i = 270$, $\sum x_i^2 = 23845$, $\sum y_i^2 = 12976$, $\sum x_i y_i = 17135$, $n = 6$

(b) $\sum x_i = 357.7$, $\sum y_i = 278.7$, $\sum x_i^2 = 11696.95$, $\sum y_i^2 = 7119.71$, $\sum x_i y_i = 8396.1$, $n = 12$

(c) $\sum x_i = 22.09$, $\sum y_i = 49.7$, $\sum x_i^2 = 45.04$, $\sum y_i^2 = 244.83$, $\sum x_i y_i = 97.778$, $n = 12$

5 For each of the following data sets plot a scatter diagram, and then calculate the product-moment correlation coefficient.

(a)

x	1	2.3	3.6	2.1	4.8	3.1	4	0.5
y	6.2	9.1	16.8	7	19.3	12.4	16	3.8

(b)

x	125	159	285	210	152	243	279	116	181	162	236
y	75	70	54	63	68	56	50	77	68	73	56

6 Use a method of coding to calculate the product-moment correlation coefficient for each of the following sets of data.

(a)

x	1503	1508	1517	1511	1520
y	45.2	55.1	60.2	58.3	65

(b)

x	297.1	286.4	290.2	288.4	293.1	300
y	43.2	48.7	46.1	47.2	46.1	41

(c)

x	0.0015	0.0018	0.0013	0.0016	0.0011
y	100.4	100.8	100.3	100.9	100.4

7 Compute the product-moment correlation coefficient for the following data giving values for S_{xx}, S_{yy} and S_{xy}.

x	2	3	4	4	5	5	6
y	7	6	5	4	3	2	1

8 (a) State the effect on the product-moment correlation coefficient between two variables x and y of
(i) changing the origin of x
(ii) changing the units of x.

(b) The following information was obtained about 8 children.

Child	A	B	C	D	E	F	G
Arithmetic mark	50	45	33	25	18	17	4
English mark	30	35	17	21	14	10	3

Calculate the product-moment correlation coefficient and use it to comment on the statement 'Those who do well at Arithmetic also do well at English'.

9 The ages X (years) and heights Y (cm) of 11 members of a football team were recorded and the following statistics were used to summarise the results.

$$\sum X = 168, \; \sum Y = 1275, \; \sum XY = 20\,704, \; \sum X^2 = 2585$$
$$\sum Y^2 = 320\,019$$

(a) Calculate the product-moment correlation coefficient for these data.
(b) Comment on the assertion that height and weight are positively correlated.

10 The following data relate to the percentage of unemployment and percentage change in wages over several years.

% Unemployment (x)	1.6	2.2	2.3	1.7	1.6	2.1	2.6	1.7	1.5	1.6
% Change in wages (y)	5.0	3.2	2.7	2.1	4.1	2.7	2.9	4.6	3.5	4.4

(a) Calculate the values of S_{xx}, S_{yy}, S_{xy} and the product-moment correlation coefficient between x and y.
(Use $\sum x = 18.9$; $\sum y = 35.2$; $\sum x^2 = 37.01$;
$\sum y^2 = 132.22$; $\sum xy = 64.7$.)
It has been suggested that low unemployment and a low rate of wage inflation cannot exist together.
(b) Without further calculation use your correlation coefficient to explain briefly whether or not you think the suggestion is justified. [E]

11 In a study on health a clinic investigated the age A (years), weight w (kg) and diastolic blood pressure p (mm of mercury) of a number of men, with the following results.

Age (A)	19	35	51	24	58	45	27	33	69
Weight (w)	66.7	55.2	76.2	66.7	75.0	101.6	60.3	69.9	63.9
Blood pressure (p)	55	60	80	85	75	85	70	85	85

Calculate the product-moment correlation coefficient between
(a) weight and blood pressure (b) age and blood pressure.
State what can be concluded from these calculations.

12 Explain briefly your understanding of the term 'correlation'.
Twelve students sat two Biology tests, one theoretical and one
practical. Their marks are shown below.

Marks in theoretical test (t)	5	9	7	11	20	4	6	17	12	10	15	16
Marks in practical test (p)	6	8	9	13	20	9	8	17	14	8	17	18

(a) Draw a scatter diagram to represent these data.
(b) Find, to 3 decimal places,
 (i) the value of S_{tp}
(ii) the product-moment correlation coefficient. [E]

13 With the help of scatter diagrams, explain the meaning of
(a) positive correlation
(b) negative correlation
(c) perfect correlation
between two variables. Describe, briefly, how you used, or
could have used, correlation in a project or in class work.

In a training scheme for young people, the times they took to
reach a required standard of proficiency were measured. The
average training time in days for each age was recorded and
the results are shown.

Age of trainees and their average training times.

Age, x(years)	16	17	18	19	20	21	22	23	24	25
Average training time, y(days)	8	6	7	9	8	11	9	10	12	11

Find the product-moment correlation coefficient between average training time and age of trainee. State whether or not your result leads you to conclude that there is a linear association between age of trainee and average training time.

[E]

14 Eight students were asked to estimate the weight of a bag of tomatoes in ounces. First they were asked to estimate without touching the bag and then they were told to pick the bag up and estimate again. The results are shown in the table below.

Student	A	B	C	D	E	F	G	H
Not touching	25	18	32	27	21	35	28	30
Holding bag	16	11	20	17	15	26	32	20

(a) Draw a scatter diagram to represent these data.
(b) Work out the product-moment correlation coefficient for these data.
(c) What conclusion can you draw from r?

15 Two branches of a small newsagents chain were close to each other on a main road. It was thought that possibly sales in one might be affecting sales in the other. Since no other shop sold sweets in the vicinity it was decided to compare sweet sales to see if this was true. Sales of sweets were recorded weekly in pounds for seven weeks. The data collected are given in the following table.

Week	1	2	3	4	5	6	7
Newsagent X	380	402	370	365	410	392	385
Newsagent Y	560	543	564	573	550	554	540

(a) Using a method of coding work out the product-moment correlation coefficient.
(b) What conclusions can you draw about sales?

SUMMARY OF KEY POINTS

1   Product-moment correlation coefficient:

$$r = \frac{S_{xy}}{\sqrt{S_{xx}S_{yy}}}$$

where

$$S_{xy} = \sum (x_i - \bar{x})(y_i - \bar{y}) = \sum x_i y_i - \frac{\sum x_i \sum y}{n}$$

$$S_{xx} = \sum (x_i - \bar{x})^2 = \sum x_i^2 - \frac{(\sum x_i)^2}{n}$$

$$S_{yy} = \sum (y_i - \bar{y})^2 = \sum y_i^2 - \frac{(\sum y_i)^2}{n}$$

2   r is a measure of linear association

$r = 1 \Longrightarrow$ perfect positive linear correlation

$r = -1 \Longrightarrow$ perfect negative linear correlation

$r = 0 \Longrightarrow$ no linear correlation

Regression

7.1 Linear regression

In the physical sciences we often set up investigations or experiments in which we try to find a relationship between two variables. For example, in your science work you may have done an experiment to investigate the relationship between the mass x hung on a spring and its length y. The purpose of such investigations is to find a law connecting the variables x and y that allows you to predict the value of y for any given value of x.

Explanatory and response variables

In the spring experiment you can choose values for the mass x and observe the resulting values of the length y. If there is a relationship between the variables then the y values are said to depend on the x values. For this reason y is called the **response variable**. The values of x are only dependent on the experimenter's choice so x is called the **explanatory variable**. (Sometimes the response variable is called the dependent variable and the explanatory variable is called the independent variable.)

We usually assume that we can set the values of the explanatory variable accurately but that our observations of the values of the response variable will be subject to some level of error or natural variation.

Scatter diagrams

One way of seeing if there is a relationship between the explanatory and response variables is to plot the points (x_i, y_i), for $i = 1$ to n, on a diagram known as a scatter diagram. When drawing a scatter diagram, the explanatory variable is always plotted horizontally and the response variable is plotted vertically.

Here are some results from an experiment in which different masses were placed on a spring and the resulting length measured:

Mass, x (kg)	20	40	60	80	100
Length, y (cm)	48	55.1	56.3	61.2	68

When plotted on a scatter diagram these data look like this:

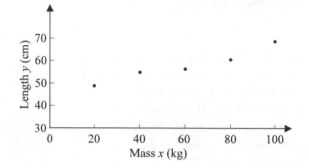

From the scatter diagram it looks as though a straight line could represent the relationship between the variables for the range of values given in the tables. (You may recall from your science work that there is a straight-line relationship known as Hooke's Law.) But in the diagram you can see that not all the points will fit onto a straight line. This is because of the errors in the measurements of the length y.

By looking at scatter diagrams you may be able to see if a straight line would be a good model for the relationship between x and y or whether a curve is more appropriate. Here are three possible models:

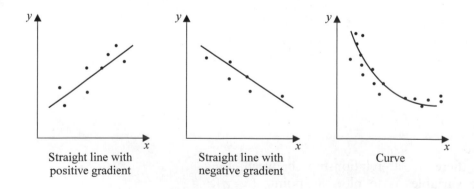

Straight line with positive gradient

Straight line with negative gradient

Curve

In this chapter we will consider only relationships in which a straight line is the appropriate model. This is called a **linear relationship**. We start by looking at the straight-line law.

The straight-line law $y = a + bx$

All straight-line laws may be defined by an equation of the form $y = a + bx$ where a and b are constants; for example, if a is 5 and b is 3 then $y = 5 + 3x$ is a straight line.

For the equation $y = a + bx$, when $x = 0$, $y = a$. Also when $x = 1$, $y = a + b$. The graph of the equation looks like this:

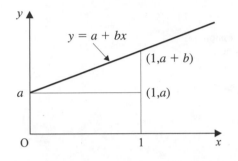

In the diagram you can see that $(0, a)$ is the point at which the line cuts the y-axis. We call this the **y-intercept**. As the coordinates of the point where $x = 1$ are $(1, a + b)$, the gradient of the line is

$$\text{gradient} = \frac{\text{change in } y}{\text{change in } x} = \frac{(a + b) - a}{1 - 0} = b$$

So b is the **gradient** of the line. To look at it in a different way, b is the amount by which the response variable y increases for an increase of 1 in the explanatory variable x.

If b is positive, y increases as x increases and the gradient is said to be positive. If b is negative, y decreases as x increases and the gradient is said to be negative.

7.2 The linear regression model

When the results of an investigation are modelled by the straight-line law, each of the values y_i will have an associated experimental error ε_i which may be positive or negative. Each y_i is expressed in terms of x_i as

$$y_i = \alpha + \beta x_i + \varepsilon_i$$

where α and β are constants.

The errors ε_i occur due to natural variations and are equally spread about a mean value of zero.

- **The linear regression model:**

$$y_i = \alpha + \beta x_i + \varepsilon_i$$

Having assumed the linear regression model, the experimental results are used to find a **regression line** which has the equation $y = a + bx$ where a and b are estimates of α and β. This regression line is known as the **regression line of y on x** since y is the response for a given value of x.

If you assume a linear regression line, each point with coordinates (x_i, y_i) will be a vertical distance r_i from the regression line as shown below. The r_i are known as **residuals**.

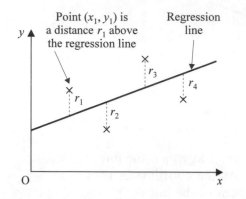

If the residuals are very small a line may be drawn through the points by eye, and this is sometimes done. A much better solution is to find the **line of best fit** using the method of least squares. The method of least squares was formulated by the French mathematician Legendre, and the resulting line is known as the **least squares regression line**.

7.3 The least squares regression line

The least squares regression line is drawn through the points representing the observations in such a way that the sum of the squares of the vertical distances between the line and the points plotted $(\sum r_i^2)$ is minimised.

The derivation of the formulae for finding a and b is outside your present syllabus but from the above diagram you can see that

$$r_i = y_i - a - bx_i$$
$$r_i^2 = (y_i - a - bx_i)^2$$
$$\sum r_i^2 = \sum (y_i - a - bx_i)^2$$

and it is $\sum (y_i - a - bx_i)^2$ that is minimised. The minimised value for b is given by the equation:

$$b = \frac{\sum (x_i - \bar{x})(y_i - \bar{y})}{\sum (x_i - \bar{x})^2}$$

In the previous chapter you defined

$$S_{xx} = \sum(x_i - \bar{x})^2$$

$$S_{yy} = \sum(y_i - \bar{y})^2$$

$$S_{xy} = \sum(x_i - \bar{x})(y_i - \bar{y})$$

Thus:

■
$$b = \frac{S_{xy}}{S_{xx}}$$

a may be found by:

$$y_i = a + bx_i$$

$$\sum y_i = na + b\sum x_i$$

$$\frac{\sum y_i}{n} = a + b\frac{\sum x_i}{n} \qquad\qquad \text{(dividing by } n)$$

$$a = \frac{\sum y_i}{n} - b\frac{\sum x_i}{n} \qquad\qquad \text{(by transposition)}$$

$$a = \bar{y} - b\bar{x} \qquad \left(\text{since } \bar{y} = \frac{\sum y_i}{n} \text{ and } \bar{x} = \frac{\sum x_i}{n}\right)$$

■ **The equation of the regression line of *y* on *x* is:**

$$y = a + bx$$

where
$$b = \frac{S_{xy}}{S_{xx}} \text{ and } a = \bar{y} - b\bar{x}$$

Remember that you will not be asked to prove these equations but you must know and be able to use the resulting formulae.

Example 1

(a) Explain, very briefly, the method of least squares for obtaining the equation of a regression line.

(b) The number of grams *g* of a certain detergent which will dissolve in 100 g of water at temperature $t°C$ is shown in the table.

t (°C)	0	10	20	30	40	50	60	70	80	90	100
g (g)	53.5	59.5	65.2	70.6	75.5	80.2	85.5	90.0	95.0	99.2	104.0

Obtain the equation of the least squares regression line of *g* on *t*.
Estimate the value of *g* for a temperature of 45°C.　　　[E]

(a)

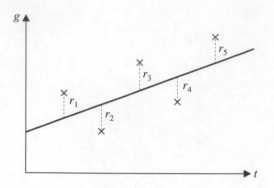

The lengths shown are the residuals r_i, $i = 1, 2, \ldots, n$.

In the least squares method the $\sum r_i^2$ is minimised.

(b)

t_i	g_i	$t_i g_i$	t_i^2
0	53.5	0	0
10	59.5	595	100
20	65.2	1304	400
30	70.6	2118	900
40	75.5	3020	1600
50	80.2	4010	2500
60	85.5	5130	3600
70	90.0	6300	4900
80	95.0	7600	6400
90	99.2	8928	8100
100	104.0	10 400	10 000
$\sum t_i = 550$	$\sum g_i = 878.2$	$\sum t_i g_i = 49\,405$	$\sum t_i^2 = 38\,500$

$$S_{tg} = \sum t_i g_i - \frac{\sum t_i \sum g_i}{n} = 49\,405 - \frac{550 \times 878.2}{11} = 5495$$

$$S_{tt} = \sum t_i^2 - \frac{(\sum t_i)^2}{n} = 38\,500 - \frac{550 \times 550}{11} = 11\,000$$

$$b = \frac{S_{tg}}{S_{tt}} = \frac{5495}{11\,000}$$

$$= 0.4995 \ (4 \text{ d.p.})$$

$$a = \bar{g} - b\bar{t}$$

$$= \frac{878.2}{11} - \frac{0.4995 \times 550}{11}$$

$$= 54.86 \ (2 \ \text{d.p.})$$

Then the regression line of g on t is $g = 54.86 + 0.4995t$

If $t = 45$
$$g = 54.86 + 0.4995 \times 45$$

$$= 77.34 \ °\text{C} \ (2 \, \text{d.p.})$$

In the example the calculation has been laid out in a tabular form so that you can see what is going on. You may instead calculate the required values of a and b by using a calculator. It is suggested that if you use a calculator then you should show sufficient working and not simply write down the answer. If you get the answer wrong you will then be given credit for any correct work done. Example 1 might appear as:

$$\sum t_i = 550 \qquad \sum g_i = 878.2$$

$$\bar{t} = 50 \qquad \bar{g} = 79.836$$

$$\sum t_i g_i = 49\,405 \qquad \sum t_i^2 = 38\,500$$

$$S_{tg} = 49\,405 - \frac{550 \times 878.2}{11} = 5495$$

$$S_{tt} = 38\,500 - \frac{550 \times 550}{11} = 11\,000$$

$$b = \frac{S_{tg}}{S_{tt}} = \frac{5495}{11\,000}$$

$$= 0.4995$$

$$a = \bar{g} - b\bar{t}$$

$$= 79.836 - \frac{0.4995 \times 550}{11}$$

$$= 54.86$$

If $t = 45$
$$g = 54.86 + 0.4995 \times 45$$
$$= 77.34 \ °\text{C}$$

7.4 Application and interpretation

Now that you have a model for your results in the form of a regression line, it is possible to use the equation of the regression line to make estimates of the mean value of the response variable for any given value of the explanatory variable within the range of the data. This process is called **interpolation**. You must remember, however, that you do not know what happens *outside* the range of your experimental values. In the case of the spring experiment mentioned earlier, there is a mass which, when applied to the spring, causes it to break, and long before this load is reached the linear relationship fails to hold. When values of the response variable are predicted using values of the explanatory variable outside the range of the experimental results the process is called **extrapolation**. You should not, in general, extrapolate and you must view any extrapolated values with caution.

When looking at the straight-line law earlier in the chapter you will have seen that a is the intercept of the line on the y-axis (the value of y when $x = 0$) and b is the gradient of the line (the amount by which y increases for an increase of 1 in x, sometimes called the rate of change of y with respect to x). These may have some meaning within the context of the investigation you are making, and you should be prepared to interpret them, as is done in the next example.

Example 2

A scientist working in agricultural research believes that there is a linear relationship between the amount of a certain food supplement given to hens and the hardness of the shells of the eggs they lay. As an experiment, controlled quantities of the supplement were added to the hens' normal diet and the hardness of the shells of the eggs was then measured on a scale from 1 to 10, with the following results:

Food supplement, f (g/day)	2	4	6	8	10	12	14
Hardness of shells, g	3.2	5.2	5.5	6.4	7.2	8.5	9.8

(a) Find the equation of the regression line of g on f.
(b) Explain what the values of a and b tell you and why you should not try to calculate the shell hardness for a food supplement of 20 g per day.

(a)
$$\sum f_i = 56 \qquad \sum g_i = 45.8$$
$$\bar{f} = 8 \qquad \bar{g} = 6.543$$
$$\sum f_i^2 = 560 \qquad \sum f_i g_i = 422.6$$
$$S_{fg} = 422.6 - \frac{56 \times 45.8}{7} = 56.2$$
$$S_{ff} = 560 - \frac{(56)^2}{7} = 112$$

$$b = \frac{S_{fg}}{S_{ff}} = \frac{56.2}{112}$$

$$= 0.5018 \text{ hardness units per g per day}$$

$$a = \bar{g} - b\bar{f}$$

$$= 6.543 - 0.5018 \times 8$$

$$= 2.5286 \text{ hardness units}$$

$$g = 2.53 + 0.502f$$

(b) a tells you the eggshell strength when no supplement is given (i.e. when $f = 0$). Zero is only just outside the range of f so it is quite reasonable to use this value. b tells you the rate at which the hardness increases with increased food supplement, in this case for every extra 1 g of food supplement per day the hardness increases by 0.5018 hardness units. The value of 20 g for f is well outside the range of f and would be very unreliable.

Having looked at both correlation and regression you can see that they are linked. Within the S1 question paper a clear distinction will be made between regression and correlation. You should realise that while regression is concerned with finding a linear relationship between two variables, the value of one variable (the response) depending for its value upon that of the other variable (the explanatory), correlation is concerned with how strongly two variables are linearly associated. In the case of correlation each variable may also depend upon one or more other variables. If you look at example 2 in chapter 6, which is looking at the strength of the relationship between distance from the centre of a city (d) and population density (p), then other factors such as the nearness of a park, or of local shopping, may also influence the density of housing, and these factors would also have an effect on the population density.

Exercise 7A

1 A linear regression line is calculated to predict the length of a spring (y cm) when a mass (x g) is suspended from it. The equation of the line is $y = 0.04x + 16.2$.

(a) Interpret the number 16.2.

(b) Interpret the number 0.04.

(c) If a mass of 750 g is suspended from the spring, what will be the length of the spring?

2 A company that has been trading for 30 years decides to look at past trends and to use a regression line calculated from past data on annual merit and inflation rises to decide pay rates for the future. This means that every employee will be able to predict their future pay. For one particular job it is decided to use the formula $y = 750x + 10\,250$, where x is the number of years service and y is the annual salary rate in £s.

(a) Write down the starting salary for a new employee under this scheme.

(b) How much rise per year would an employee get?

(c) What would be the annual salary of an employee after 10 years?

(d) An employee who has already been working for the firm for 30 years has an annual salary of £20 000. He thinks he is being underpaid. Explain whether or not he has reasonable grounds for demanding a pay rise.

(e) One of the managers thinks that there are inherent faults in using this formula. Do you think she is right? Give reasons for your answer.

3 Find the equation of the regression line of y on x for the following data:

x	2	4	5	8	10
y	3	7	8	13	17

4 The relationship between the number of coats of paint applied to a yacht and the resulting weather resistance was tested in a laboratory. One year's weathering on the yacht was simulated by one month's corrosion in the laboratory. The table shows the results of this experiment, when one month's corrosion is changed to 1 year's weathering on the yacht.

Coats of paint (x)	1	2	3	4	5
Protection (years) (y)	1.4	2.9	4.1	5.8	7.2

Find the equation of the regression line for protection on coats of paint.

5 For the following data

(a) find the mean values $\bar{x}$ and $\bar{y}$, and using these find the equation of the regression line of y on x.

(b) Plot a scatter diagram and draw the regression line of y on x.

x	6	8	10	12	14
y	102	106	110	113	120

6 (a) By plotting a scatter diagram for the following data suggest a possible relationship between x and y.

(b) Find the equation of the least squares regression line for these data. Give values for S_{xy} and S_{xx}.

x	10	20	30	40	50	60	70
y	16	14.8	14.6	11.6	13.1	11.0	9.7

7 The variables H and T are known to be linearly related. Fifty pairs of experimental observations of the two variables gave the following results:

$$\sum H = 83.4 \qquad \sum T = 402.0 \qquad \sum HT = 680.2$$
$$\sum H^2 = 384.6 \qquad \sum T^2 = 3238.2$$

Obtain the regression equation from which one can estimate H when T has the value 7.8, and give, to 1 decimal place, the value of this estimate. [E]

8 The accountant of a company monitors the number of items produced per month by the company, together with the total cost of production. The following table shows the data collected for a random sample of 12 months.

Number of items (x) $(1000s)$	21	39	48	24	72	75	15	35	62	81	12	56
Production cost (y) $(£1000)$	40	58	67	45	89	96	37	53	83	102	35	75

(a) Plot these data on a scatter diagram. Explain why this diagram would support the fitting of a regression equation of y on x.

(b) Find an equation for the regression line of y on x in the form $y = a + bx$.

$$\left(\text{Use } \sum x^2 = 30\,786; \quad \sum xy = 41\,444.\right)$$

The selling price of each item produced is £2.20.

(c) Find the level of output at which total income and total costs are equal. Interpret this value. [E]

9 A drilling machine can run at various speeds, but in general the higher the speed the sooner the drill needs to be replaced. Over several months, 15 pairs of observations relating to speed, s revolutions per minute, and life of drill, h hours, are collected. For convenience the data are coded so that $x = s - 20$ and $y = h - 100$ and the following summations obtained:

$$\sum x = 143; \sum y = 391; \sum x^2 = 2413; \sum y^2 = 22\,441;$$
$$\sum xy = 484$$

(a) Find the equation of the regression line of h on s.
(b) Interpret the slope of your regression line.
(c) Estimate the life of a drill revolving at 30 revolutions per minute. [E]

10 The table below shows the age A and the strontium ratio S for each of 10 basalt rock samples, one sample of each age being specifically chosen for the exercise.

Ages and strontium ratios of rock samples

A (10^2 Ma)	1	2	3	4	5
S	0.710	0.723	0.738	0.751	0.765

A (10^2 Ma)	6	7	8	9	10
S	0.780	0.793	0.808	0.824	0.840

Find the values of $\bar{A}$ and $\bar{S}$.
Given that $\sum AS = 43.710$, obtain the equation of the regression line of strontium ratio on age.
Estimate the strontium ratio for a basalt rock sample of age 3.5×10^2 Ma. [E]

11 Distinguish between the explanatory and the response variables in a linear regression.

In an experiment, the atomic heat, H units, of an element was measured at various temperatures, T degrees absolute (degrees Kelvin). The results are shown in the table:

T	100	150	200	250	300	350	400	450	500
H	0	0.38	0.8	1.22	1.6	2	2.42	2.8	3.18

Draw a scatter diagram to exhibit the data. Mark the means of T and H on your diagram.

Given that $\sum TH = 5520$, obtain the equation of the regression line of atomic heat on absolute temperature.

From your equation, estimate the increase in the atomic heat of the element when its temperature is increased by 100 degrees absolute. [E]

12 The value of the variable y for different values of x is given in the table below:

x	2	3	4	5	6	7
y	0.204	0.218	0.189	0.269	0.172	0.142

x	8	9	10	11	12	13
y	0.149	0.111	0.125	0.123	0.112	0.096

It is thought that the model relating y and x could be of the form

$$y = a + bx$$

(a) Plot a scatter diagram of y against x.

(b) Ignoring the observation $(5, 0.269)$, find the equation of the regression line in the above form, giving the coefficients to 3 significant figures.

(You may use $\sum y = 1.641$)

13 A farm food supplier monitors the number of hens kept, x,
against the weekly consumption of food, y kg, for a sample of
10 smallholdings.

The results are summarised below.

$$\sum x = 360, \quad \sum x^2 = 17362, \quad \sum y = 286$$
$$\sum y^2 = 10928.94, \quad \sum xy = 13773.6$$

(a) Obtain the regression equation for y on x in the form
$y = a + bx$.

(b) Give a practical interpretation of the slope b.

(c) If food costs £7.50 for a 25 kg bag, estimate the weekly
cost of feeding the hens. [E]

14 In a chemical reaction it is known that the amount, A grams,
of a certain compound produced is a linear function of the
temperature, T degrees Celsius. Eight trial runs of this
reaction are performed, two at each of four different
temperatures. The observed values of A are subject to error.
The results are shown.

T	10	15	20	25
A	10	15	18	16
	12	12	16	20

Draw a scatter diagram for these data.

Calculate the means of A and T.

Obtain the equation of the regression line of A on T, giving
the coefficients to two decimal places.

Draw this line on your scatter diagram.

Use the regression equation to obtain an estimate of the mean
value of A when $T = 20$, and explain why this estimate is
preferable to averaging the two observed values of A when
$T = 20$.

Estimate the mean increase in A for a one degree increase in
temperature.

State any reservations you would have about estimating A
when $T = 0$. [E]

15 A sixth form head needs to predict the grades his students will get in their final examination. To do this he decides to look at the marks gained in mock examinations. He thinks that in Mathematics there is a linear relationship between these marks. To investigate this he looks at the results of students from past years. The mock examination and average final examination marks are given in the following table.

Mock mark	18	26	28	34	36	42	48	52	54	60
Av. final mark	54	64	54	62	68	70	76	66	76	74

If x represents the mock mark and y the average final mark:

(a) draw a scatter diagram to represent these data,

(b) Find the equation of the regression line in the form $y = a + bx$.

(c) (i) What final marks might be expected for mock marks of: 30, 16, 50, 85?

(ii) Comment on the validity of these predicted final marks.

SUMMARY OF KEY POINTS

1 **Explanatory or independent variable:**
a variable that is set independently of the other variable.

2 **Response or dependent variable:**
the variable whose values are decided by the values of the explanatory or independent variable.

3 **Linear regression model:**
$y_1 = \alpha + \beta x_i + \varepsilon_i$

4 **The regression line of y on x is:**
$$y = a + bx,$$

where $\quad b = \dfrac{S_{xy}}{S_{xx}} \quad$ and $\quad a = \bar{y} - b\bar{x}$

Discrete random variables

8

8.1 Concept of a random variable

Earlier in your mathematical studies you may have come across problems like this:

> "Mrs Brown bought 4 grapefruit and 2 melons from her grocer. A melon costs 60p more than a grapefruit and her total bill was £2.94. What was the cost of a grapefruit?"

A common approach to problems such as this is to introduce a **variable** x, which represents the cost in pence of a grapefruit, and then form an equation in x:

$$4x + 2(x + 60) = 294.$$

This equation can then be solved to obtain $x = 29$.

In this chapter you will be considering situations where the variable could take one of several possible values. It may not be possible to say for sure which value is going to arise in a particular situation but the aim is to be able to state how likely it is. In other word, to state the **probability** that a particular value will occur.

A statistician decided to introduce an element of probability into the weekly pocket money he gave his son. The son rolled a fair die and whatever the value on the uppermost face of the die his father gave him that many pounds for his pocket money that week. Thus, a roll of 5 on the die meant that the boy received £5 pocket money that week. If M represents the value in pounds of the son's pocket money for next week then M is a **random variable**. Capital letters, like M, are used to describe random variables and a lower case letter, such as m, is used to represent a particular value of the random variable.

- **A random variable X is a variable that represents the value obtained when we take a measurement from an experiment in the real world. A random variable must take a numerical value.**

(In the above example the experiment would be rolling the die to establish the weekly pocket money.)

8.2 The probability function

Notice that in the previous example the answer to "*M*" will be a number but it is not possible to say what that number will be. However, you know that *M* has to be one of the six numbers 1, 2, 3, 4, 5 or 6 (all the numbers on the faces of the die) and, since the die is fair, you can assign a probability, in this case $\frac{1}{6}$ everytime, to each of these values. The set of all possible values of a random variable together with the associated probabilities is called a **probability distribution** and the function that describes how the probabilities are assigned is called the **probability function**. In the case of the pocket money, the probability function is:

$$P(M = m) = \tfrac{1}{6} \qquad m = 1, 2, \ldots, 6$$

and the probability distribution is written as:

m:	1	2	3	4	5	6
P(*M* = *m*):	$\frac{1}{6}$	$\frac{1}{6}$	$\frac{1}{6}$	$\frac{1}{6}$	$\frac{1}{6}$	$\frac{1}{6}$

Since the probability function describes how probability is assigned to *all* possible values then the sum of the P(*M* = *m*) values equals 1, in this case this is simply:

$$\sum_{m=1}^{6} \tfrac{1}{6} = 1$$

This property of the probability function often provides a check that a probability distribution has been properly defined.

For a random variable *X* the probability function P(*X* = *x*) is sometimes written as **p(*x*)**. The different notations are freely interchangeable, and in most cases we will use the former.

Types of random variable

The statistician's son bought some new batteries for his walkman and they were advertised as giving between 5 and 8 hours of continuous play. Let *H* represent the number of hours these new batteries will last. *H* is another random variable. Notice that there is an important difference between *M* (as defined above) and *H*. The random variable *M* can take any *whole* number value (between 1 and 6) but *M* = 5.43 is not possible. The random variable *M* is called a **discrete random variable** – one which changes *by steps* and therefore only takes some values in the interval [1,6]. In general, a discrete random variable can only take specified values within a given range. On the other hand *H* could take *any* value (inside the advertised range of values, called the interval [5,8]). *H* is a **continuous random variable**. The probability distribution for a continuous random variable cannot be described in terms of a simple probability function. You cannot talk about the probability of a single value, for example, $P(H) = 7$, but rather a range of values, for example, $P(H \geqslant 7)$. This will be discussed in greater depth in Book S2 but in this chapter we shall only be dealing with discrete random variables.

The important property of discrete random variables is summarised below.

■ **If X is a discrete random variable with probability function $P(X = x)$, or $p(x)$ then:**

$$\sum_{\forall x} P(X = x) = 1$$

> The symbol $\forall x$ means for all values of x.

Example 1

A tetrahedral die has the numbers 1, 2, 3 and 4 on its faces. The die is biased in such a way that the probability of the die landing on the number n is inversely proportional to n, for example:

$$P(\text{die lands on } 3) = \frac{k}{3}$$

where k is a constant.

Find the probability distribution for X, the number the die lands on after a single roll.

The distribution of X will be:

x:	1	2	3	4
$P(X = x)$:	$\frac{k}{1}$	$\frac{k}{2}$	$\frac{k}{3}$	$\frac{k}{4}$

Since this is a probability distribution, $\sum P(X = x) = 1$.

∴ $\qquad k(1 + \frac{1}{2} + \frac{1}{3} + \frac{1}{4}) = 1$

i.e. $\qquad k\left(\frac{12+6+4+3}{12}\right) = 1$

∴ $\qquad k = \frac{12}{25}$

So the probability distribution of X is:

x:	1	2	3	4
$P(X = x)$:	$\frac{12}{25}$	$\frac{6}{25}$	$\frac{4}{25}$	$\frac{3}{25}$

8.3 The cumulative distribution function

In chapter 2 cumulative frequency polygons were discussed and here the same idea is extended to probability distributions. The cumulative distribution function is defined as follows:

- The **cumulative distribution function** $F(x_0)$ of the random variable X is:

$$F(x_0) = P(X \leqslant x_0)$$

If X has a discrete distribution then $F(x_0)$ is simply given by:

$$F(x_0) = \sum_{x \leqslant x_0} P(X = x)$$

We shall see in S2 that there are tables of the cumulative distribution function for certain probability distributions. These can be quite useful but it is in connection with continuous random variables that the cumulative distribution function (c.d.f.) is most useful.

Example 2

(a) Find the values of $F(1)$ and $F(3)$ for the cumulative distribution of the tetrahedral die in example 1.
(b) Hence find $P(2 \leqslant X \leqslant 3)$.
(c) Find $F(2.7)$.

(a) From the above $P(X \leqslant 1) = \frac{12}{25}$, $P(X \leqslant 3) = \frac{12}{25} + \frac{6}{25} + \frac{4}{25} = \frac{22}{25}$

(b) $P(2 \leqslant X \leqslant 3) = P(X \leqslant 3) - P(X \leqslant 1)$

$$= \frac{22}{25} - \frac{12}{25}$$
$$= \frac{10}{25} = \frac{2}{5}$$

(c) $F(2.7) = P(X \leqslant 2.7)$
$\quad\quad\quad = P(X \leqslant 2)$
$\quad\quad\quad = F(2) = \frac{12}{25} + \frac{6}{25} = \frac{18}{25}$

N.B. We do not interpolate here since we are dealing with a discrete random variable.

Exercise 8A

1 A discrete random variable X has the following probability distribution:

x:	1	2	3	4
$P(X = x)$:	$\frac{1}{3}$	$\frac{1}{3}$	k	$\frac{1}{4}$

where k is a constant.
(a) Find the value of k.   (b) Find $P(X \leqslant 3)$.

2 The discrete random variable Y has the following probability distribution:

y:	-1	0	1
$P(Y = y)$:	a	$\frac{1}{4}$	a

where a is a constant.
(a) Find the value of a.   (b) Find $P(Y \geqslant 0)$.

3 State which of the following could describe discrete probability distributions and give the value of x when a probability distribution is defined.

(a)

a:	-2	-1	0	1	2
$P(A = a)$:	$\frac{1}{4}$	$\frac{1}{4}$	x	$\frac{1}{6}$	$\frac{1}{6}$

(b)

b:	0	$\frac{1}{2}$	1
$P(B = b)$:	0.4	x	0.4

(c)

c:	1	2	3	4
$P(C = c)$:	x	$\frac{2}{3}$	x	$\frac{1}{2}$

4 The random variable X has the following probability distribution:

x:	1	5	9
$P(X = x)$:	a	b	c

where a, b and c are constants.

It is known that $P(X < 4) = P(X > 4)$ and $P(X \leqslant 5) = 2P(X > 5)$.

(a) Find the values of a, b and c.

(b) Find F(8).

5 A cubical die is biased in such a way that the probability is proportional to the number showing, for example, $P(\text{die lands on } 5) = 5k$, where k is a constant. Find the probability distribution for S, the score on the die.

6 Two tetrahedral dice have the numbers 1, 2, 3 and 4 on their faces. The dice are thrown together. Let $S =$ the sum of their two scores and let $D =$ the difference between their two scores.

(a) Show that $P(S = 6) = \frac{3}{16}$.

(b) Find the probability distribution for the random variable S.

(c) Find $P(S \leqslant 7)$

(d) Show that $P(D = 1) = \frac{3}{8}$.

(e) Find the probability distribution for the random variable D.

(f) Find $P(D \geqslant 2)$.

7 Sam's pocket contains one £1 coin, one 50p coin and three 20p coins. He selects 2 coins at random to place in a collection box. The random variable X represents the amount, in pence, that he puts in the box.

(a) Show that $P(X = 70) = 0.3$.

(b) Find the probability distribution for X.

8 A fair coin is tossed repeatedly until a head appears or 3 tosses have been made. The random variable T represents the number of tosses.

(a) Show that $P(T = 2) = \frac{1}{4}$.

(b) Find the probability distribution of T.

The random variable H represents the number of heads.

(c) Find the probability distribution of H.

9 Which of the following could be discrete random variables. If they could not explain why.

(a) A bag contains 20 red, 20 blue and 10 yellow beads.

(i) Four beads are selected and $R =$ the number of red beads selected.

(ii) Four beads are selected and $F =$ the colour of the fourth bead selected.

(iii) Beads are selected until a blue bead is found and $B =$ the number of beads selected.

(b) A pupil is selected at random from a class.

(i) $E =$ the colour of their eyes.

(ii) $S =$ the number of letters in their surname.

(iii) $A =$ their age in completed years.

(iv) $B =$ the number of brothers they have.

10 The discrete random variable X has c.d.f. $F(x)$ defined by

$$F(x) = \frac{2 + x}{7}; \ x = 1, 2, 3, 4 \text{ and } 5.$$

(a) Find $P(X \leqslant 3)$.

(b) Show that $P(X = 4) = \frac{1}{7}$.

(c) Find the probability distribution for X.

11 The discrete random variable X has c.d.f. $F(x)$ defined by

$$F(x) = \frac{2x + 1}{9}; \ x = 0, 1, 2, 3, \text{ and } 4.$$

(a) Find $F(3)$.

(b) Show that $P(X = 2) = \frac{2}{9}$.

(c) Find the probability distribution for X.

12 The discrete random variable X has c.d.f. $F(x)$ defined by

$$F(x) = \frac{(x+k)^2}{16}; \; x = 1, 2 \text{ and } 3.$$

(a) Find the value of k.

(b) Find the probability distribution for X.

13 The discrete random variable X has probability function given by:

$$P(X = x) = \begin{cases} (\frac{1}{2})^x, & x = 1, 2, 3, 4, 5, \\ C, & x = 6, \\ 0, & \text{otherwise,} \end{cases}$$

where C is a constant.

Determine the value of C. [E]

14 A darts player practises throwing a dart at the bull's-eye on a dart board. Independently for each throw, her probability of hitting the bull's-eye is 0.2. Let X be the number of throws she makes, up to and including her first success.

(a) Find the probability that she is successful for the first time on her third throw.

(b) Write down an equation for the probability distribution of X.

(c) Find the probability that she will have at least 3 failures before her first success. [E]

15 Six fuses, of which two are defective and four are good, are to be tested one after another in random order until both defective fuses are identified. Find the probability that the number of fuses that will be tested is:

(a) three.

(b) four or fewer. [E]

8.4 The concept of expectation for discrete random variables

In example 1, the probability distribution for the discrete random variable X, representing the score on a biased tetrahedral die, was found to be:

x:	1	2	3	4
$P(X = x)$:	$\frac{12}{25}$	$\frac{6}{25}$	$\frac{4}{25}$	$\frac{3}{25}$

Consider the following problem: if you were to throw the die 100 times then how many 3s would you expect to obtain? Since $P(X = 3) = \frac{4}{25}$ then 4 times in every 25 throws you would expect a 3 to occur. So, in 100 throws you might expect $100 \times \frac{4}{25} = 16$ occasions when a 3 occurs. In practice, of course, you may well not obtain exactly 16 threes. The 16 reflects the distribution of X which you are using as a model for this practical experiment. These 100 "theoretical" throws will give rise to the following expected frequency table:

x:	1	2	3	4
Expected frequency:	48	24	16	12

To find the mean for the population of x values, use $\mu = \dfrac{\sum fx}{\sum f}$ which gives

$$\frac{1 \times 48 + 2 \times 24 + 3 \times 16 + 4 \times 12}{100} = 1.92$$

A closer look at this calculation shows that the number of throws is irrelevant. If you treat the values of $P(X = x)$ as frequencies you obtain the same result:

$$\frac{1 \times \frac{12}{25} + 2 \times \frac{6}{25} + 3 \times \frac{4}{25} + 4 \times \frac{3}{25}}{\sum P(X = x) \ (= 1)} = \frac{48}{25} = 1.92$$

and this value is called the **mean of X** or **expected value of X**. The expected value of X is usually written as $E(X)$ and sometimes the Greek letter mu, μ is used for the mean value of a random variable.

In general, for a discrete random variable X:

■ **Expected value of X**

$$\mu = E(X) = \sum_{\forall x} x P(X = x)$$

The **expectation of a *function* of a random variable** can be considered in a similar way. Suppose you again throw this biased tetrahedral die and instead of recording the score X, you record $2X - 1$. If you let this new variable be Y then you can ask, what is $E(Y)$? The distribution is:

x:	1	2	3	4
y:	1	3	5	7
$P(Y = y)$:	$\frac{12}{25}$	$\frac{6}{25}$	$\frac{4}{25}$	$\frac{3}{25}$

Notice how the probabilities relating to X are still being used, for example, $P(Y = 7) = P(X = 4)$. Now

$$E(Y) = 1 \times \tfrac{12}{25} + 3 \times \tfrac{6}{25} + 5 \times \tfrac{4}{25} + 7 \times \tfrac{3}{25}$$
$$= \tfrac{71}{25}$$
$$= 2.84$$

This is:

$$\sum y P(Y = y) = \sum (2x - 1)P(X = x)$$

$$= 2 \sum x P(X = x) - \sum P(X = x)$$

$$= 2E(X) - 1$$

This is equivalent to:

$$E(2X - 1) = 2E(X) - 1$$

which is an example of a general result that will be dealt with in the next section.

You can also find $E(X^2)$ in a similar way. The distribution is:

x:	1	2	3	4
x^2:	1	4	9	16
$P(X = x)$:	$\frac{12}{25}$	$\frac{6}{25}$	$\frac{4}{25}$	$\frac{3}{25}$

and

$$E(X^2) = \sum x^2 P(X = x)$$

$$= 1^2 \times \tfrac{12}{25} + 2^2 \times \tfrac{6}{25} + 3^2 \times \tfrac{4}{25} + 4^2 \times \tfrac{3}{25}$$

$$= \tfrac{120}{25}$$

$$= 4.8$$

Notice that

$$E(X^2) \neq [E(X)]^2$$

In general, you can find the expected value of a function of a random variable $g(X)$ as follows:

- $E[g(X)] = \displaystyle\sum_{\forall x} g(x)P(X = x)$

In Book S1 we shall consider only linear functions of X or the simple case of X^2 for finding the variance.

You can now find the **variance of a random variable** X, $\text{Var}(X)$. In chapter 4, the population variance was defined as:

$$\frac{\sum f(x - \mu)^2}{\sum f}$$

which was equivalent to:

$$\frac{\sum f x^2}{\sum f} - \mu^2$$

So using the probabilities as frequencies again you have:

$$\text{Var}(X) = \sum_{\forall x} (x - \mu)^2 P(X = x)$$
$$= \sum_{\forall x} x^2 P(X = x) - \mu^2$$

So for your tetrahedral die:

$$\text{Var}(X) = 4.8 - (1.92)^2$$
$$= 1.1136$$

The Greek letter sigma, σ, is used to represent the **standard deviation** of a random variable and so you have:

$$\sigma^2 = \text{Var}(X)$$

■ **Variance of X**

$$\textbf{Var}(X) = \sum_{\forall x} (x - \mu)^2 \textbf{P}(X = x)$$
$$= \sum_{\forall x} x^2 \textbf{P}(X = x) - \mu^2$$

or
$$\sigma^2 = \textbf{Var}(X) = \textbf{E}(X^2) - \mu^2$$

Example 3

Two fair cubical dice are thrown: one is red and one is blue. The random variable M represents the score on the red die minus the score on the blue die.

(a) Find the distribution of M.
(b) Write down E(M).
(c) Find Var(M).

(a) You can represent the value of M in the following table:

Red \ Blue	1	2	3	4	5	6
1	0	−1	−2	−3	−4	−5
2	1	0	−1	−2	−3	−4
3	2	1	0	−1	−2	−3
4	3	2	1	0	−1	−2
5	4	3	2	1	0	−1
6	5	4	3	2	1	0

$\therefore$ m:	−5	−4	−3	−2	−1	0	1	2	3	4	5
P($M = m$):	$\frac{1}{36}$	$\frac{2}{36}$	$\frac{3}{36}$	$\frac{4}{36}$	$\frac{5}{36}$	$\frac{6}{36}$	$\frac{5}{36}$	$\frac{4}{36}$	$\frac{3}{36}$	$\frac{2}{36}$	$\frac{1}{36}$

(b) By symmetry, $E(M) = 0$.

(c) $Var(M) = \sum_{m=-5}^{5} m^2 P(M = m) - 0^2$

$= 25 \times \frac{1}{36} + 16 \times \frac{2}{36} + 9 \times \frac{3}{36} + \ldots + 0 + 1 \times \frac{5}{36} + \ldots + 25 \times \frac{1}{36}$

$= \frac{(25 + 32 + 27 + 16 + 5) \times 2}{36}$

$= \frac{105}{18}$

$= \frac{35}{6}$

Exercise 8B

1 Find the mean and variance for each of the following
   distributions of X:

   (a)

x:	1	2	3
$P(X = x)$:	$\frac{1}{3}$	$\frac{1}{2}$	$\frac{1}{6}$

   (b)

x:	−1	0	1
$P(X = x)$:	$\frac{1}{4}$	$\frac{1}{2}$	$\frac{1}{4}$

   (c)

x:	−2	−1	1	2
$P(X = x)$:	$\frac{1}{3}$	$\frac{1}{3}$	$\frac{1}{6}$	$\frac{1}{6}$

2 Given that Y is the score when a single unbiased cubical die is
   rolled, find $E(Y)$ and $Var(Y)$.

3 Two fair cubical die are rolled and S is the sum of their scores.
   (a) Find the distribution of S.   (b) Write down $E(S)$.
   (c) Find $Var(S)$.

4 Two fair cubical die are rolled and D is the difference
   between their scores.
   (a) Show that $P(D = 3) = \frac{1}{6}$ and find the distribution of D.
   (b) Find $E(D)$.   (c) Find $Var(D)$.

5 A fair die is rolled and the random variable N represents the
   number showing. A square of side N is then drawn on a piece
   of paper.
   (a) Find the expected value of the area of this square.
   (b) Find the variance of the perimeter of this square.

6 A fair coin is tossed twice and the random variable H
   represents the number of heads recorded.
   (a) Find the distribution of H.   (b) Write down $E(H)$.
   (c) Calculate $Var(H)$.

7 A fair coin is tossed repeatedly until a head appears or 3 tosses have been made. The random variable T represents the number of tosses of the coin.

(a) Show that the distribution of T is:

t:	1	2	3
$P(T = t)$:	$\frac{1}{2}$	$\frac{1}{4}$	$\frac{1}{4}$

(b) Find the mean and variance of T.

8 A statistically-minded parent is discussing pocket money with a young child. The parent has a £1 and a 50p coin. Both coins are spun and if a coin lands with heads uppermost the child can have it as pocket money, otherwise the parent keeps it. The child's parent is generous and, rather than disappointing the child, in the event of both coins landing tails the child will receive 50p. How much pocket money can the child expect to receive?

9 The random variable X has the following distribution:

x:	1	2	3
$P(X = x)$:	a	b	a

where a and b are constants.

(a) Write down $E(X)$.

(b) Given that $Var(X) = 0.75$, find the values of a and b.

10 At a fair a roll-a-penny stall can be played with 1p or 2p coins. If the coin lands inside a square (without touching the edges) the player receives the coin plus 2 other coins of the same value, otherwise the coin is lost. The probability of winning the prize with a 1p coin is $\frac{19}{40}$ and the probability for a 2p coin is $\frac{11}{40}$.

(a) Find the expected winnings for each coin.

(b) Would you play this game and why?

(c) The stall was eventually closed down by the management. Give a possible reason for this.

11 The random variable X has probability function

$$P(X = x) = \begin{cases} \frac{c}{x}, & x = 1, 2, ..., 6, \\ 0, & \text{otherwise}, \end{cases}$$

where c is a constant. Find the value of:

(a) c (b) $E(X)$ (c) $Var(X)$.   [E]

12 A box A contains 9 red balls and one white ball. A box B contains 8 red balls and one white ball. A ball is to be taken at random from box A and put into box B, and then a ball is to be taken at random from box B. Find the probability that this ball from box B will be white.

Of the 2 balls drawn, one from A and one from B, let X denote the number that are white. Find the probability distribution of X.

Find the mean of X.

Find also, to 2 decimal places, the variance of X.   [E]

13 A random variable R takes the integer value r with probability p(r), where:

$$p(r) = kr^3 \qquad r = 1, 2, 3, 4$$
$$p(r) = 0 \qquad \text{otherwise.}$$

Find

(a) the value of k, and display the distribution on graph paper.

(b) the mean and the variance of the distribution.   [E]

8.5 Expectation of a linear function of a random variable

The concept of the expected value of X considered earlier in this chapter can be extended to deal with the expected value of a function of X and the following definition is used:

$$E[g(X)] = \sum g(x)\,P(X = x)$$

where p$(X = x)$ is the probability function for a discrete random variable X. There are certain properties of expected value and variance which are fairly easy to verify in specific cases and are particularly useful. They are:

■

$$E(aX) = aE(X)$$
$$E(aX + b) = aE(X) + b$$
$$\text{Var}(aX) = a^2\text{Var}(X)$$
$$\text{Var}(aX + b) = a^2\text{Var}(X)$$

If X is a **discrete random variable** and a and b are constants, a little thought should enable you to appreciate why the last result is true. The variance is a measure of spread relative to the mean so adding a constant value to all the values of X will not affect this measure of spread hence the "b" does not change the variance. The "a^2" is understandable if you remember that:

$$\text{Var}(X) = E(X^2) - [E(X)]^2$$

so if each value of X is multiplied by the value of a the variance will be multiplied by a^2.

Example 4

Two 10p coins are tossed. The random variable X represents the total value of each coin that lands heads up.

(a) Find $E(X)$ and $\text{Var}(X)$.

The random variables S and T are defined as follows:

$$S = X - 10 \quad \text{and} \quad T = \tfrac{1}{2}X - 5$$

(b) Show that $E(S) = E(T)$.
(c) Find $\text{Var}(S)$ and $\text{Var}(T)$.

Susan and Thomas play a game using two 10p coins. The coins are tossed and Susan records her score using the random variable S and Thomas uses the random variable T. After a large number of tosses they compare their scores.

(d) Comment on any likely differences or similarities.

(a) Firstly find the distribution of X.

x:	0	10	20
$P(X = x)$:	$\frac{1}{4}$	$\frac{1}{2}$	$\frac{1}{4}$

$E(X) = 20 \times \frac{1}{4} + 10 \times \frac{1}{2} + 0 \times \frac{1}{4} = 10$ (or use symmetry)

$\text{Var}(X) = 20^2 \times \frac{1}{4} + 10^2 \times \frac{1}{2} + 0^2 \times \frac{1}{4} - 10^2 = 50$

(b) $E(S) = E(X) - 10 = 10 - 10 = 0$

$E(T) = \frac{1}{2}E(X) - 5 = \frac{1}{2} \times 10 - 5 = 0$

(c) $\text{Var}(S) = \text{Var}(X) = 50$

$\text{Var}(T) = \left(\frac{1}{2}\right)^2 \text{Var}(X) = \frac{50}{4} = 12.5$

(d) Their total scores should both be approximately zero. Susan's scores should be more varied than Thomas's.

Exercise 8C

1 The random variable Y has mean 2 and variance 9.
   Find the following:
   (a) $E(3Y + 1)$ (b) $E(2 - 3Y)$ (c) $\text{Var}(3Y + 1)$
   (d) $\text{Var}(2 - 3Y)$ (e) $E(Y^2)$ (f) $E[(Y-1)(Y+1)]$

2 The random variable X has mean μ and standard deviation σ.
Find the following in terms of μ and σ:

(a) $E(3X)$ (b) $E(2X + 3)$ (c) $E(3 - 2X)$

(d) $\text{Var}(2X + 3)$ (e) $\text{Var}(3 - 2X)$ (f) $E(X^2)$

3 The random variable T has mean 20 and standard deviation
5. It is required to scale T by using the transformation
$S = aT + b$, where a and b are constants ($a > 0$), so that $E(S)$
and $\text{Var}(S)$ satisfy specified values. Find the values of a and b
in each of the following cases:

(a) $E(S) = 0$ and $\text{Var}(S) = 1$

(b) $E(S) = 100$ and $\text{Var}(S) = 225$

(c) $E(S) = 50$ and $\text{Var}(S) = 100$

(d) $E(S) = 5$ and $\text{Var}(S) = 25$

4 A spinner is made from the disc in the diagram and the
random variable X represents the number it lands on after
being spun.

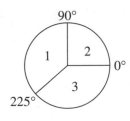

(a) Write down the distribution of X.

(b) Write down $E(X)$.

(c) Find $\text{Var}(X)$.

Ann and Bill use this spinner to play a board game. Ann
records her score using the random variable $2X - 1$, and Bill
records his using the random variable $3X - 3$.

(d) Show that their mean scores are the same.

(e) Find the variances of each player's scores.

5 Sam is 6 years old and Ruth is 4. To calculate their weekly
pocket money they each select a coin at random from a bag
containing 7 ten pence coins and 3 twenty pence coins. Their
pocket money is calculated by multiplying the value of their
coin by their age, and then adding twice their age.
Find how much each child can expect to receive each week.

6 The discrete random variable X has probability distribution
specified by the following table.

x	-2	0	2	4
$P(X = x)$	0.3	0.4	0.2	0.1

(a) Find $E(X)$.

(b) Find $Var(X)$.

(c) Find $E(\frac{1}{2}X + 1)$.

(d) Find $Var(\frac{1}{2}X + 1)$.

7 The discrete random variable X has the probability
distribution specified in the following table:

x	-1	0	1	2
$P(X = x)$	0.25	0.10	0.45	0.20

(a) Find $P(-1 \leqslant X < 1)$ (b) Find $E(2X + 3)$.   [E]

8 The discrete random variable R has probability function
$p(r) = P(R = r)$ defined by:

$$p(0) = p(6) = \tfrac{1}{16}, \ p(1) = p(4) = \tfrac{1}{4}$$

$$p(3) = \tfrac{3}{8}, \ p(r) = 0 \text{ elsewhere.}$$

Find $E(R)$ and $Var(R)$.

Find the mean and the variance of

(a) $2R - 5$

(b) $R_1 - R_2$, where R_1 and R_2 are independent observations
of R.   [E]

8.6 The discrete uniform distribution

In section 8.2 you considered the probability distribution for the
score S on a single roll of a fair die, namely:

s:	1	2	3	4	5	6
$P(S = s)$:	$\frac{1}{6}$	$\frac{1}{6}$	$\frac{1}{6}$	$\frac{1}{6}$	$\frac{1}{6}$	$\frac{1}{6}$

This is an example of a **discrete uniform distribution** over the set
$\{1, 2, 3, 4, 5, 6\}$.

This distribution is easily generalised so that if the discrete random
variable X is defined over the set of distinct values $\{x_1, x_2, x_3, \ldots x_n\}$,
and each value is equally likely, then X has a discrete uniform
distribution and

$$P(X = x_r) = \frac{1}{n} \qquad r = 1, 2, 3 \ldots n$$

Conditions for a discrete uniform distribution:

- **The discrete random variable X is defined over a set of n distinct values.**
- **Each value is equally likely.**
- **$X =$ the value of the next outcome.**

This distribution, despite its simplicity, arises in a number of instances but care should be taken to ensure that the above conditions are applicable. For example, a table of random digits is designed so that each digit is equally likely. So, if the random variable R represents the value of the next digit in the table, then R will have a discrete uniform distribution over the set $\{0, 1, 2, 3, \ldots 9\}$ and R should be a good model for such a table.

Consider the following example. A bag contains five coins one 50p, one 10p, one 20p, one 2p and one 5p. You place your hand in the bag and pick out the first coin you feel. The random variable V represents the value of that coin. You could try and model V as a discrete uniform distribution over the set $\{2, 5, 10, 20, 50\}$. Is this a suitable model, as a 50p coin is much larger than a 5p one?

It is not clear that the probability of selecting the 50p coin is the same as that for the 5p coin. You could use the discrete uniform distribution as a preliminary model, collect some experimental data and test how well this data fits the model. If the model does not provide a particularly good fit then the model can be refined, perhaps by making the probability proportional to the surface area of the coins.

In general, the mean and variance of the discrete uniform random variable X which is defined over the set $\{1, 2, 3, \ldots n\}$ can be found using the results:

$$\sum_{r=1}^{n} r = \frac{n(n+1)}{2} \qquad \text{and} \qquad \sum_{r=1}^{n} r^2 = \frac{n}{6}(n+1)(2n+1)$$

as follows:

$$E(X) = \sum_{r=1}^{n} rP(X=r)$$

$$= \sum_{r=1}^{n} r \times \frac{1}{n}$$

$$= \frac{1}{n} \sum_{r=1}^{n} r \qquad \text{since } n \text{ does not depend on } r$$

$$= \frac{1}{n} \times \frac{n(n+1)}{2}$$

i.e. $\qquad \mu = E(X) = \dfrac{n+1}{2}$

This result is, of course, obvious by the symmetry of the distribution.

$$\text{Var}(X) = \sum_{r=1}^{n} r^2 P(X = r) - \mu^2$$

$$= \frac{1}{n} \sum_{r=1}^{n} r^2 - \frac{(n+1)^2}{4}$$

$$= \frac{1}{n} \times \frac{n}{6}(n+1)(2n+1) - \frac{(n+1)^2}{4}$$

$$= \frac{(n+1)}{12}[2(2n+1) - 3(n+1)]$$

i.e. $\quad\quad \sigma^2 = \text{Var}(X) = \dfrac{(n+1)(n-1)}{12}$

Example 5

Digits are selected at random from a table of random digits.

(a) Write down the mean and standard deviation of the value of a single digit.

(b) Find the probability that a particular digit lies within one standard deviation of the mean.

Let R represent a random variable having a discrete uniform distribution over the set $\{0, 1, 2, \ldots 9\}$. This should model the value of a random digit.

Let X represent a random variable having a discrete uniform distribution over the set $\{1, 2, 3, \ldots 10\}$. Since the probability functions for X and R are both equal to $\frac{1}{10}$ there is a simple relationship between X and R, namely $X = R + 1$. You can use the general formulae derived above for X with $n = 10$.

(a) $\quad\quad\quad\quad \text{E}(R) \;=\; \text{E}(X - 1)$

$$= \text{E}(X) - 1$$

$$= \frac{10 + 1}{2} - 1$$

$$= 4.5$$

and

$$\text{Var}(R) = \text{Var}(X - 1)$$

$$= \text{Var}(X)$$

$$= \frac{11 \times 9}{12}$$

$$= \frac{33}{4}$$

$$= 8.25$$

So the standard deviation is:

$$\sigma = \sqrt{8.25}$$
$$= 2.87 \text{ (3 s.f.)}$$

(b) Using the value of σ in (a), the required probability is:

$$P(1.62\ldots < R < 7.37\ldots) = P(2 \leqslant R \leqslant 7)$$
$$= \tfrac{6}{10}$$

Exercise 8D

1 A fair die is thrown once and the random variable X represents the value on the uppermost face.
   (a) Find the mean and variance of X.
   (b) Calculate the probability that X is within one standard deviation of the mean.

2 Repeat question 1 for an icosohedral die (20 faces) with the numbers 1 to 20 on the faces.

3 A card is selected at random from a pack of 10 cards containing the even numbers 2, 4, 6,... 20 and the random variable X represents the number on the card.
   (a) Find $P(X \geqslant 15)$.
   (b) Find the mean and variance of X.

4 Repeat question 3 for the odd numbers 1, 3, 5,... 19.

5 A straight line is drawn on a piece of paper. The line is divided into quarters and the segments are numbered 1, 2, 3 and 4. In a certain party game a person is blind folded and asked to mark a point on the line and the number of the segment in which their point lies is recorded. A discrete uniform distribution over the set $\{1, 2, 3, 4\}$ is suggested as a model for this distribution. Comment on this suggestion.

6 A dart board consists of a circle divided into 20 equal-sized sectors marked with the numbers 1, 2,... 20. A dart is thrown to land in the sector marked 20. If the dart misses the board it is thrown again. A discrete uniform distribution over the set $\{1, 2, \ldots 20\}$ is suggested as a model to describe the number of the sector in which the dart lands. Comment on this suggestion.

7 In a T.V. game a contestant is asked to choose one of five plain brown envelopes. One envelope contains a blank piece of paper, one a £5 note, one a £10 note, one a £20 note and the last one contains a £50 note. Discuss whether a discrete uniform distribution could be used to model this situation.

8 Given that X is the number showing when a fair die is thrown, name the distribution of X, and write down its probability function.

Determine the values of $E(X)$ and $Var(X)$.   [E]

SUMMARY OF KEY POINTS

1 For a **discrete random variable** X

$$\sum_{\forall x} P(X = x) = 1$$

$$\mu = E(X) = \sum_{\forall x} x P(X = x)$$

$$\sigma^2 = E(X^2) - \mu^2 = \sum_{\forall x} x^2 P(X = x) - \mu^2$$

2 **Properties of expected values and variance**

$$E(aX + b) = aE(X) + b$$

$$Var(aX + b) = a^2 Var(X)$$

3 **Cumulative distribution function F(x)**

$$0 \leqslant F(x) \leqslant 1$$

4 **For the *discrete* random variable X:**

$$F(x_0) = P(X \leqslant x_0) = \sum_{x \leqslant x_0} P(X = x)$$

The normal distribution

9

9.1 The normal distribution

If you sit in the lounge of a busy airport and watch people going about their business one of the features you will notice is the variation in the heights of these people. Some will be quite short, others very tall, but for both men and women you will find that most heights cluster about a central value, say 178 cm for the men and 163 cm for the women. If you were to measure the heights of a large sample of both men and women and then represent these heights by means of a histogram you might obtain histograms as follows.

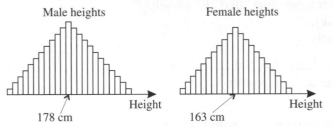

Notice that both distributions are approximately symmetrical and both have fewer and fewer observations as the distribution moves away from the central value. In this practical situation you would expect this. How many people have you seen over 213 cm tall or shorter than 122 cm?

Earlier in the book (page 148) a continuous random variable was introduced as being one that can take any value in a given range. Height is such a variable and, whilst a relative frequency histogram is a useful method of representing a continuous random variable, it would be useful for us to have a statistical distribution as a model for continuous random variables which are distributed like those above.

The distribution used is the **normal distribution**. Dating back to the seventeenth and eighteenth centuries the normal distribution is the most important distribution in statistics. Unfortunately it is a distribution that has a complicated mathematical form and much of the mathematics associated with it is beyond the scope of this book. Fortunately you do not need to know any of the mathematics, but you should be familiar with the shape of the distribution and its properties.

For a continuous random variable X which follows a normal distribution or is normally distributed a sketch of its distribution is shown below:

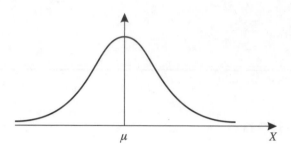

From this sketch the properties of a normal distribution can be summarised as:

- **The distribution is symmetrical about the mean μ.**
- **The mode, median and mean are all equal, due to the symmetry of the distribution.**
- **The range of X is from $-\infty$ to $+\infty$.**
- **The horizontal axis is asymptotic to the curve as $x \to -\infty$ and $x \to +\infty$. (An asymptote is a straight line that is closely approached but never met by a curve).**
- **The total area under the curve is unity.**

It is beyond the scope of this book to show that the last property is true, but it is of paramount importance that you know that it is true.

The normal distribution is a two-parameter distribution, the parameters being μ, its mean and σ, its standard deviation. You should recognise these from earlier parts of this book. Earlier reference was made to the fact that there is a link between μ and σ^2 and that it would be made in chapter 9. The link is that they are the two parameters fundamental to the most important distribution in statistics. The practical implications of this link will be seen later in this chapter, but it can be shown that the probability of X depends *only* on μ and σ^2 and it will be sufficient for you to refer to the random variable X as having a normal distribution by using the notation:

$$X \sim \mathrm{N}(\mu, \sigma^2)$$

The first parameter in the brackets is the mean, μ, and the second one is the variance, σ^2. Proofs that $\mathrm{E}(X) = \mu$ and $\mathrm{Var}(X) = \sigma^2$ are beyond the scope of this book but it is important for you to remember them and to become competent in their use in the above notation. In practice these two parameters, μ and σ^2, determine the shape of a normal distribution as is illustrated below.

Let $X_1 \sim \mathrm{N}(\mu_1, \sigma^2)$ and $X_2 \sim \mathrm{N}(\mu_2, \sigma^2)$ $\mu_1 < \mu_2$

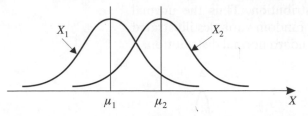

As can be seen, these two distributions have different location parameters but the same dispersion.

Let $Y_1 \sim N(\mu, \sigma_1^2)$ and $Y_2 \sim N(\mu, \sigma_2^2)$ $\qquad \sigma_1^2 < \sigma_2^2$

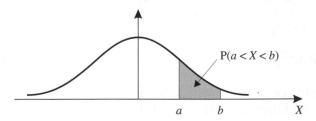

In this case the two distributions have the same location parameter but different dispersions.

Since the normal distribution is used to model continuous random variables, then if you need to evaluate probabilities associated with this distribution it is necessary to evaluate areas under the normal curve. Thus if $X \sim N(\mu, \sigma^2)$ then $P(a < X < b)$ is evaluated as the area under the normal curve between a and b. A sketch, as shown below, is helpful to illustrate the appropriate area.

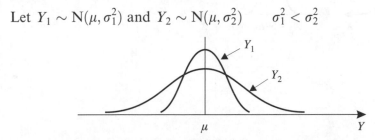

Unfortunately this area cannot be evaluated using standard techniques and in order to carry out such an evaluation you need to refer to statistical tables which have been derived for just that purpose.

9.2 The standard normal distribution

To evaluate probabilities associated with normal distributions the **standard normal distribution** is used which, as its name implies, has all the properties of a normal distribution but in addition it has a mean of zero and a standard deviation of 1. The **standard normal random variable** is denoted by Z where $Z \sim N(0, 1^2)$ and the important feature of this distribution is that *any normal distribution* can be mapped onto the standard normal distribution. Thus the normal distributions corresponding to the three random variables illustrated below can each be transformed into a standard normal distribution.

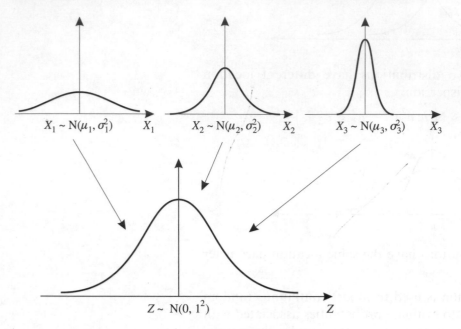

This transformation is achieved by subtracting the mean and dividing by the standard deviation. Hence:

$$Z = \frac{X - \mu}{\sigma} \qquad \text{where } X \sim N(\mu, \sigma^2) \text{ and } Z \sim N(0, 1^2).$$

Thus if $X \sim N(100, 15^2)$ then

$$Z = \frac{X - 100}{15} \sim N(0, 1^2)$$

Since *any* normal random variable can be transformed into a standard normal variable then if probabilities for the standard normal variable can be found then this property can be used to evaluate probabilities associated with normal distributions.

If, for example, you wish to evaluate $P(12 < X < 16)$ where $X \sim N(10, 4^2)$ then using $Z = \dfrac{X - 10}{4}$ gives:

$$P(12 < X < 16) = P\left(\frac{12 - 10}{4} < \frac{X - 10}{4} < \frac{16 - 10}{4}\right)$$
$$= P(0.5 < Z < 1.5)$$

To evaluate such a probability it is necessary to introduce a special symbol $\Phi(z)$ where z is the particular value of Z and $\Phi(z)$ represents the area to the left of any given z value. Thus $\Phi(1.6) = P(Z < 1.6)$ and is equal to the area under the standard normal curve between $-\infty$ and 1.6.

So for the probability above:

$$P(12 < X < 16) = P(0.5 < Z < 1.5)$$
$$= \Phi(1.5) - \Phi(0.5)$$

When evaluating probabilities such as these you are strongly advised to draw appropriate diagrams to ensure that you are clear in your own mind exactly which areas under the normal curve you need to evaluate. An illustration is given below showing how $P(12 < X < 16)$, where $X \sim N(10, 4^2)$ would be evaluated.

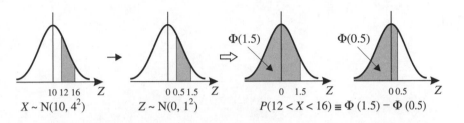

Evaluation of $\Phi(z)$ is very difficult but, fortunately values of $\Phi(z)$ have been extensively tabulated and you will find a number of different formats for these tabulations. The table 1 on page 197 of this book tabulates $\Phi(z)$ for values of z in the interval (0.00, 4.00) giving values of $\Phi(z)$ in the interval (0.5000, 1.0000). Thus if you now turn to page 197 and evaluate $P(12 < X < 16)$ you will find:

$$P(12 < X < 16) = P(0.5 < Z < 1.5)$$
$$= \Phi(1.5) - \Phi(0.5)$$
$$= 0.9332 - 0.6915$$
$$= 0.2417$$

Since the table only gives values of $\Phi(z)$ for z in the interval (00.0, 4.00), to get values of $\Phi(z)$ in the interval $(-4.00, 0.00)$ you need to remember that any normal distribution is symmetrical about its mean and in particular the standard normal distribution is symmetrical about zero, i.e. $\Phi(0.00) = 0.500$. This will then enable you to find values such as $\Phi(-1.2)$ as illustrated below.

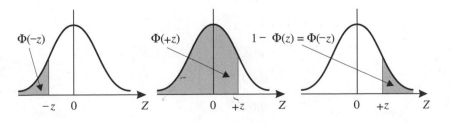

From this illustration you can see that:

$$\Phi(-z) = 1 - \Phi(z)$$

Hence:

$$\Phi(-1.2) = 1 - \Phi(1.2)$$
$$= 1 - 0.8849$$
$$= 0.1151$$

As with most techniques, the more you practice them the easier their use becomes and you *must* become familiar with the use of tables of $\Phi(z)$. **Good clear diagrams will always help.**

Example 1

Given that $Z \sim N(0, 1^2)$, find:

(a) $P(Z > 1.0)$
(b) $P(Z < -2.0)$
(c) $P(-1.5 < Z < 0.5)$

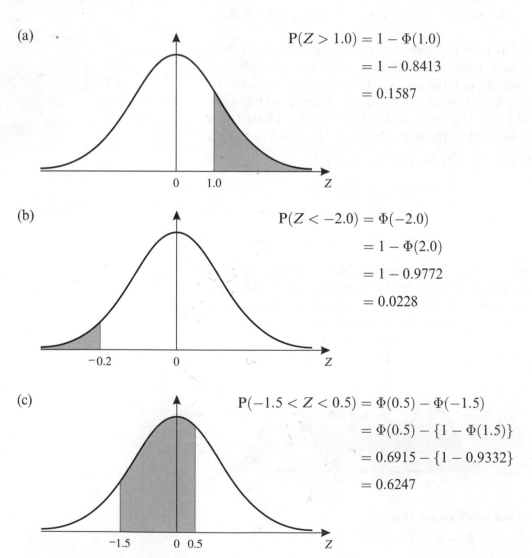

(a)

$$P(Z > 1.0) = 1 - \Phi(1.0)$$
$$= 1 - 0.8413$$
$$= 0.1587$$

(b)

$$P(Z < -2.0) = \Phi(-2.0)$$
$$= 1 - \Phi(2.0)$$
$$= 1 - 0.9772$$
$$= 0.0228$$

(c)

$$P(-1.5 < Z < 0.5) = \Phi(0.5) - \Phi(-1.5)$$
$$= \Phi(0.5) - \{1 - \Phi(1.5)\}$$
$$= 0.6915 - \{1 - 0.9332\}$$
$$= 0.6247$$

Example 2

Given that $Y \sim N(56, 10^2)$, find:

(a) $P(Y > 68)$
(b) $P(56 < Y < 65)$
(c) $P(42 < Y < 52)$

(a)

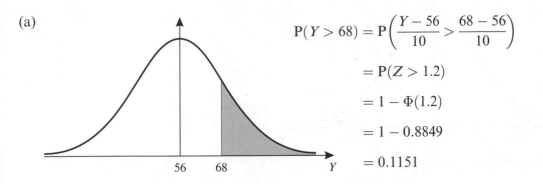

$$P(Y > 68) = P\left(\frac{Y - 56}{10} > \frac{68 - 56}{10}\right)$$

$$= P(Z > 1.2)$$

$$= 1 - \Phi(1.2)$$

$$= 1 - 0.8849$$

$$= 0.1151$$

(b)

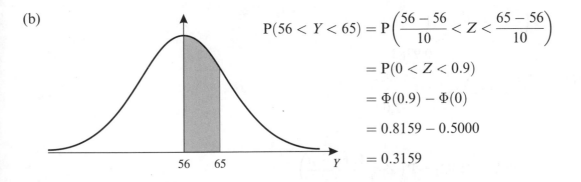

$$P(56 < Y < 65) = P\left(\frac{56 - 56}{10} < Z < \frac{65 - 56}{10}\right)$$

$$= P(0 < Z < 0.9)$$

$$= \Phi(0.9) - \Phi(0)$$

$$= 0.8159 - 0.5000$$

$$= 0.3159$$

(c)

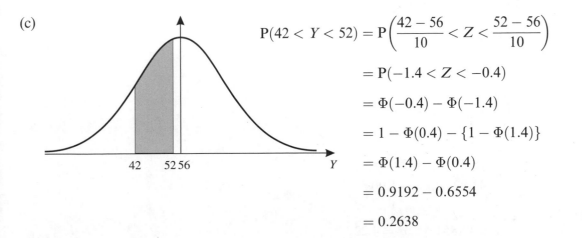

$$P(42 < Y < 52) = P\left(\frac{42 - 56}{10} < Z < \frac{52 - 56}{10}\right)$$

$$= P(-1.4 < Z < -0.4)$$

$$= \Phi(-0.4) - \Phi(-1.4)$$

$$= 1 - \Phi(0.4) - \{1 - \Phi(1.4)\}$$

$$= \Phi(1.4) - \Phi(0.4)$$

$$= 0.9192 - 0.6554$$

$$= 0.2638$$

Example 3

The random variable X is normally distributed with mean μ and variance σ^2. Given that

$$P(X > 58.39) = 0.0217 \qquad \text{and} \qquad P(X < 41.82) = 0.0287$$

find μ and σ.

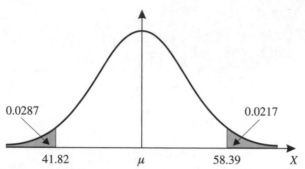

From the diagram you can see that:

$$P(X > 58.39) = P\left(Z > \frac{58.39 - \mu}{\sigma}\right)$$

$$= 0.0217$$

$$\therefore \qquad \Phi\left(\frac{58.39 - \mu}{\sigma}\right) = 1 - 0.217$$

$$= 0.9783$$

Thus from the tables:

$$\frac{58.39 - \mu}{\sigma} = 2.02$$

Similarly:

$$P(X < 41.82) = P\left(Z < \frac{41.82 - \mu}{\sigma}\right)$$

$$= 0.0287$$

$$\therefore \qquad \Phi\left(\frac{41.82 - \mu}{\sigma}\right) = 0.0287$$

$$\therefore \qquad \Phi\left\{-\left(\frac{41.82 - \mu}{\sigma}\right)\right\} = 1 - 0.0287$$

$$= 0.9713$$

$$\therefore \qquad -\left(\frac{41.82 - \mu}{\sigma}\right) = 1.90$$

Hence:

$$58.39 - \mu = 2.02\sigma$$
$$41.82 - \mu = -1.90\sigma$$

Solving gives:

$$\mu = 49.851 \qquad \sigma = 4.227$$

You will have realised that the values of z in the tables are given to two decimal places and that in the previous three examples this was adequate. Sometimes the value for z from your calculations may contain more than two decimal places. In such cases you should either round your value to two decimal places and use the table directly or you can **interpolate**. For example, if $z = 1.83$ then $\Phi(z) = 0.9664$ and if $z = 1.84$, $\Phi(z) = 0.9671$, so, if your value of z is 1.8372, then you round to 1.84 and use $\Phi(z) = 0.9671$ or:

$$\Phi(1.8372) = 0.9664 + \frac{72}{100}(0.9671 - 0.9664)$$
$$= 0.9669$$

For the purposes of the examination it is sufficient to round your value to two decimal places and read directly from the tables and thus avoid having to interpolate.

Once you become experienced at evaluating areas under the normal curve you will soon appreciate that certain areas are commonly used and that sometimes a z value corresponding to a special standard probability is needed, consequently their z values have been tabulated more accurately. Table 2 on page 198 contains z values for the standard normal variable $Z \sim N(0, 1)$ such that the random variable exceeds z with probability p. Thus:

$$P(Z > z) = 1 - \Phi(z) = p$$

From the table you will see that, for example:

$$P(Z > 1.9600) = 0.0250$$
$$P(Z > 1.6449) = 0.0500$$
$$P(Z > 3.0902) = 0.0010 \text{ etc.}$$

It is important to note that by symmetry if $P(Z > 1.9600) = 0.0250$ then $P(Z < -1.9600) = 0.0250$. As your statistical knowledge increases you will find that z-values such as 1.9600, 1.6449, etc. are values you will remember without needing to refer to the tables since they are values most commonly used by statisticians.

Example 4
The door frames used by a builder are of one standard height, 1.830 m. The heights of men are normally distributed with mean 1.730 m and standard deviation 0.064 m.
(a) Find the proportion of men that will be taller than the door frame.
(b) Find the frame height, such that one man in a thousand will be taller than the frame height.

The door frames are to be used in a department store. It is known that women outnumber men in the ratio 19:1 in the store and the proportion of women taller than the door frame is 0.00069.

(c) Find the proportion of people for whom a frame height of 1.830 m would be too low.

(a) Let M represent the heights of men, such that $M \sim N(1.73, 0.064^2)$.

$$\therefore \qquad P(M > 1.83) = P\left(Z > \frac{1.83 - 1.73}{0.064}\right)$$

$$= P(Z > 1.5625)$$

From tables, $\Phi(1.56) = 0.9406$ and $\Phi(1.57) = 0.9418$

$$\therefore \qquad \Phi(1.5625) = 0.9406 + \frac{25}{100}(0.9418 - 0.9406)$$

$$= 0.9409$$

Hence:

$$P(Z > 1.5625) = 1 - \Phi(1.5625)$$

$$= 1 - 0.9409$$

$$= 0.0591$$

(b) Let h represent the frame height, then $P(M > h) = 0.0010$.

$$\therefore \qquad P(M > h) = P\left(Z > \frac{h - 1.73}{0.064}\right)$$

$$= 0.0010$$

$$\therefore \qquad 1 - \Phi\left(\frac{h - 1.73}{0.064}\right) = 0.0010$$

As was stated earlier, 0.0010 is one of the values commonly used and can be found in Table 2 on page 198 corresponding to a z value of 3.0902.

Hence:

$$1 - \Phi(3.0902) = 0.0010$$

Thus:

$$\frac{h - 1.73}{0.064} = 3.0902$$

$$\therefore \qquad h = 1.9277728$$

i.e. $\qquad h = 1.93 \text{ to } 3 \text{ s.f.}$

(c) Since there are 19 women to every man in the store then the proportion of people for whom the frame height would be too low is given by:

$$\tfrac{19}{20}(0.00069) + \tfrac{1}{20}(0.0591) = 0.00361$$

Exercise 9A

1 The random variable $Z \sim N(0, 1^2)$. Find:
   (a) $P(Z < 1.78)$ (b) $P(Z < 2.5)$ (c) $P(Z < 0.28)$
   (d) $P(Z < 1.5)$ (e) $P(Z < 1.455)$ (f) $P(Z > 1.78)$
   (g) $P(Z > 2.5)$ (h) $P(Z > 0.28)$ (i) $P(Z > 1.5)$
   (j) $P(Z > 0.714)$

2 The random variable $Z \sim N(0, 1^2)$. Find:
   (a) $P(0.32 < Z < 1.38)$ (b) $P(1.25 < Z < 2.5)$
   (c) $P(-0.5 < Z < 0.5)$ (d) $P(-1.2 < Z < 2.1)$
   (e) $P(Z < 0.5 \text{ or } > 1.5)$ (f) $P(Z < -1.0 \text{ or } > 2.0)$

3 Find the value of z in each of the following:
   (a) $\Phi(z) = 0.9495$ (b) $\Phi(z) = 0.5910$
   (c) $\Phi(z) = 0.9660$ (d) $\Phi(-z) = 0.3783$
   (e) $\Phi(-z) = 0.1056$ (f) $\Phi(-z) = 0.0244$

4 The random variable $Z \sim N(0, 1^2)$. Find:
   (a) $P(Z > 1.25)$ (b) $P(Z < -1.0)$ (c) $P(-2.0 < Z < 1.0)$

5 For each of the following diagrams find the z value and hence
   the area of the shaded portion:

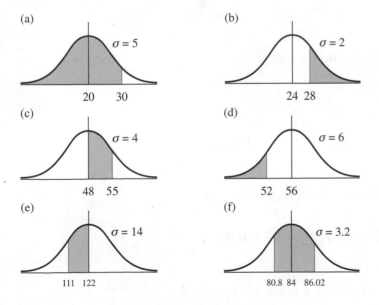

6 The random variable $A \sim N(28, 3^2)$. Find:
   (a) $P(A < 32)$ (b) $P(A > 36)$ (c) $P(28 < A < 35)$
   (d) $P(22 < A < 26)$ (e) $P(25 < A < 33)$

7 The random variable X has a normal distribution with mean 16 and variance 0.64. Find x, such that $P(X < x) = 0.025$. [E]

8 For each of the following diagrams find μ:

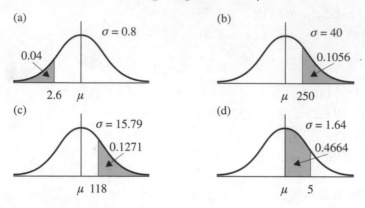

(a) $\sigma = 0.8$, 0.04, 2.6, μ

(b) $\sigma = 40$, 0.1056, μ 250

(c) $\sigma = 15.79$, 0.1271, μ 118

(d) $\sigma = 1.64$, 0.4664, μ 5

9 For each of the following diagrams find σ:

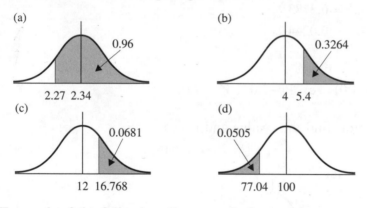

(a) 0.96, 2.27 2.34

(b) 0.3264, 4 5.4

(c) 0.0681, 12 16.768

(d) 0.0505, 77.04 100

10 For each of the following diagrams find μ and σ:

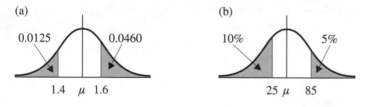

(a) 0.0125, 0.0460, 1.4 μ 1.6

(b) 10%, 5%, 25 μ 85

11 The random variable M is normally distributed with mean μ and variance σ^2.
Given that $P(M > 34) = 0.0228$ and $P(M < 25) = 0.0062$ find μ and σ.

12 The weights of steel sheets produced by a plant are known to be normally distributed with mean 31.4 kg and standard deviation 2.4 kg. Find the percentage of sheets that weigh more than 35.6 kg.

13 A machine dispenses liquid into cartons in such a way that the amount of liquid dispensed on each occasion is normally distributed with standard deviation 20 ml and mean 266 ml. Cartons that weigh less than 260 ml have to be recycled. What proportion of cartons are recycled?
Cartons weighing more than 300 ml produce no profit. What percentage of cartons will this be?

14 Boxes of chocolate with mean weight 1 kg are produced. It is decided that all boxes weighing less than 990 g and more than 1050 g will be repacked. If the weight of the boxes is normally distributed with standard deviation 20 g, what proportion of the boxes are repacked?

15 Over a long period it has been found that the breaking strains of cables produced by a factory are normally distributed with mean 6000 N and standard deviation 150 N. Find, to 3 decimal places, the probability that a cable chosen at random from the production will have a breaking strain of more than 6200 N.   [E]

16 Records from a dental practice show that the probability of waiting to go into the surgery, for more than 20 minutes is 0.0239. If the waiting time is normally distributed with standard deviation 3.78 what is the mean waiting time?

17 Batteries for a radio have a mean life of 160 hours and a standard deviation of 30 hours. Assuming the battery life follows a normal distribution, calculate:
(a) the proportion of batteries which have a life of between 150 hours and 180 hours
(b) the range (symmetrical about the mean) within which 75% of batteries lie.

18 The thickness of some sheets of wood follows a normal distribution with mean μ and standard deviation σ. 96% of the sheets will go through an 8 mm gauge while only 1.7% will go through a 7 mm gauge. Find μ and σ.

SUMMARY OF KEY POINTS

1 For a continuous random variable X, having a normal distribution,

$$\text{Mean} = \mu$$

$$\text{Variance} = \sigma^2$$

2 Given that $X \sim N(\mu, \sigma^2)$,

$$\text{then} \quad Z = \frac{X - \mu}{\sigma} \sim N(0, 1^2)$$

Review exercise 2

1 A die is thrown.
   (a) Draw up a probability distribution for the score X on the die.
   (b) What type of distribution is this?
   (c) Calculate $E(X)$ and the standard deviation.

2 Pupils on a certain course were given an aptitude test before
  the course started and a final test at the end of the course. A
  product-moment correlation coefficient of 0.94 was calculated
  for these data. Interpret this value of r.

3 The weights of packets of soap powder follow a normal
  distribution with mean 625 g and standard deviation 15 g.
  What is the probability that the contents of a randomly
  selected packet weigh more than 630 g?

4 The lifetime of a torch battery has a normal distribution with
  mean 210 hours and standard deviation 12 hours.
  Find the probability that the torch battery will last between
  205 and 215 hours.

5 If X has the distribution $N(0, 1)$ calculate
   (a) $P(X \leqslant 1.15)$,
   (b) $P(0 \leqslant X \leqslant 1.15)$.

6 A researcher looks at the total lifetime earnings and the age
  at death of a large sample of white collar workers. He
  calculates a correlation coefficient r of $+0.8$ and concludes
  that poverty causes premature death. Is this a reasonable
  conclusion to draw?

7 Shown below are three different scatter diagrams

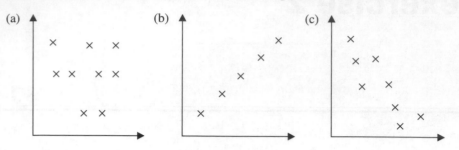

Select from the values of r given below a suitable value to go with each picture.

$$r = 0, \quad r = 0.3, \quad r = -1, \quad r = 0.96, \quad r = 1, \quad r = -0.9$$

8 The two variables M and O are thought to be connected by a relationship of the form $O = aM + b$. For set values of M the variable O took values as shown below

M	10	15	23	31	40	42	43	61	70	72	75	76
O	12	15	20	28	50	40	41	62	65	70	75	73

Calculate the equation of the regression line of O on M.

9 If Z has the distribution $N(102.3, 1.96^2)$, calculate $P(Z < 100)$.

10 A discrete random variable has the probability distribution shown in the table below.

x	1	2	3	4
$P(X = x)$	0.2	0.3	0.4	0.1

Calculate:
(a) $P(1 < X \leqslant 3)$
(b) $E(X)$
(c) $Var(X)$.

11 Apprentices for a particular building trade are graded for their ability to recognise certain pipe diameters at sight. The diameters of interest are 2 cm, 5 cm, 8 cm, 15 cm and 20 cm. A skilled trainer asked 50 apprentices to state the diameter of a piece of 8 cm piping and obtained the following results.

Diameter	2 cm	5 cm	8 cm	15 cm	20 cm
Frequency	2	9	27	11	1

An apprentice is selected at random from the group of 50 and the trainer wishes to model the error made by the apprentice when estimating the diameter of a piece of 8 cm pipe. The random variable X is the apprentice's estimate, in cm, minus 8.

(a) Use the above information to write down a probability distribution of X.

(b) Show that $E(X) = 1$.

(c) Calculate $Var(X)$.   [E]

12 The discrete random variable X has the following probability distribution:

x	0	1	2	3	4
$P(X = x)$	0.20	0.20	0.20	0.20	0.20

(a) Write down the name of the distribution of X.

(b) Calculate $P(0 \leqslant X < 2)$.

(c) Calculate $E(X)$.

13 An economics student is trying to model the daily movement, X points, in a stock market indicator. The student assumes that the value of X on one day is independent of the value on the next day. A fair die is rolled and if an odd number is uppermost then the indicator is moved down that number of points. If an even number is uppermost then the indicator is moved up that number of points.

(a) Write down the distribution of X as specified by the student's model.

(b) Calculate the value of $E(X)$.

(c) Show that $Var(X) = \frac{179}{12}$

If the indicator moves upwards over a period of time then this is taken as a sign of growth in the economy, if it falls than this is a sign that the economy is in decline.

(d) Comment on the state of the economy as suggested by this model.   [E]

14 The discrete random variable X has the probability function shown in the table below.

x	1	2	3	4	5
$P(X = x)$	0.2	0.3	0.3	0.1	0.1

Calculate:

(a) $P(2 < X \leqslant 4)$

(b) $F(3.7)$

(c) $E(X)$

(d) $Var(X)$.

15 Water chestnuts are sold in tins by a supermarket. The weight, C, of the contents of a tin is normally distributed with mean 225 g and standard deviation 12 g. Calculate the probability that the weight of the contents of a randomly chosen tin is

(a) less than 210 g

(b) not within 30 g either side of the mean weight of the contents of tins.

16 A school has pupils who live in a rural area and have to use public transport to get to school. In a study of the distance the pupils travel, a random sample of 20 journeys was taken and the distances x, in kilometres, and journey times t, in minutes, were recorded. The average distance was 4.535 km and the average journey time was 15.15 minutes.

Using $\sum x^2 = 493.77$, $\sum t^2 = 4897$, $\sum xt = 1433.8$

calculate the product moment correlation coefficient for these data.

17 In 1980 a river was restocked with fish. The local angling club kept a record of the number of fish, y, caught on a stretch of the river t years after restocking. Some of the records are given in the table below.

t	1	2	3	4	5	7	10	12
y	185	170	172	166	164	159	162	157

(a) Plot a scatter diagram of y against t.

A local conservation organisation believed that a linear regression of the form $y = p + qt$ could be used to model this situation.

(b) Give an interpretation of q.

The conservation organisation found the equation of the regression line to be $y = 177.28 - 1.89t$.

(c) Explain the long-term implications of this model for the number of fish caught.

A member of the angling club suggests an alternative model based on introducing the new variable $x = \dfrac{1}{t}$. The following statistics are calculated:

$$\sum x = 2.6095, \quad \sum y = 1335,$$
$$\sum x^2 = 1.5010, \quad \sum xy = 453.6310$$

(d) Calculate the regression equation of y on x in the form $y = a + bx$.

(e) Explain the long-term implications of his new model for the number of fish caught.

(f) Give an interpretation of the value of a.   [E]

18 If the random variable X is distributed as N(5, 4), calculate:

(a) $P(X > 0)$

(b) $P(|X - 5| > 3)$.

19 In an experiment the temperature of a metal rod was raised from 300 K. The extensions E mm of the rod at selected temperatures T K are shown in the table:

Extension of a metal rod

T	300	350	400	450	500	550	600	650	700
E	0	0.38	0.8	1.22	1.6	2	2.42	2.8	3.18

Draw a scatter diagram for these data and mark on your diagram the point representing the means of T and E.

Find the equation of the regression line of E on T and draw this line on your diagram.

Estimate the extension of the rod at 430 K.   [E]

20 (a) Draw a diagram to illustrate the lengths whose sum of squares is minimised in the least squares method for finding the regression line of y on x.

State which is the explanatory (independent) and which is the response (dependent) variable.

(b) The length (L mm) and width (W mm) of each of 20 individuals of species of fossil are measured. A summary of the results is:

$$\sum L = 400.20, \ \sum W = 176.00, \ \sum LW = 3700.20,$$
$$\sum L^2 = 8151.32, \ \sum W^2 = 1780.52$$

Obtain the product-moment correlation coefficient between the length and width of these fossils. Without performing a significance test interpret your results.

21 Climbing rope produced by a manufacturer is known to be such that one-metre lengths have breaking strengths that are normally distributed with mean 170.2 kg and standard deviation 10.5 kg. Find, to 3 decimal places, the probability that a one-metre length of rope chosen at random from those produced by the manufacturer will have a breaking strength of 175 kg to the nearest kg.   [E]

22 If the random variable $X \sim N(300, 25)$, calculate:
(a) $P(X < 312)$ (b) $P(305 < X < 312)$.

23 As part of a survey in a particular profession, age, x years, and salary, £y thousands, were recorded.

The values of x and y for a randomly selected sample of ten members of the profession are as follows:

x	30	52	38	48	56	44	41	25	32	27
y	22	38	40	34	35	32	28	27	29	41

Calculate, to 3 decimal places, the product-moment correlation coefficient between age and salary.   [E]

24 During production in a cement plant, test cubes of cement are taken at regular intervals and their compressive strengths, in kg cm^{-2}, are determined. Analysis of data over a long time has shown that compressive strength is normally distributed with a mean of 468 kg cm^{-2} and a standard deviation of

$16\,\text{kg}\,\text{cm}^{-2}$. Calculate, to 3 decimal places, the probability that a randomly chosen cube has a compressive strength:

(a) greater than $480\,\text{kg}\,\text{cm}^{-2}$

(b) between $450\,\text{kg}\,\text{cm}^{-2}$ and $475\,\text{kg}\,\text{cm}^{-2}$.   [E]

25 Two gauges are used to test the thickness of panes of glass. Over a long period it is found that 1.25% of the panes pass through the 1.4 mm gauge but 95.4% pass through the 1.6 mm gauge. Assuming the thickness of the glass follows a normal distribution find its mean and standard deviation.

26 A machine hire company kept records of the age, X months, and the maintenance costs, $£Y$, of one type of machine. The following table summarises the data for a random sample of 10 machines.

Machine	A	B	C	D	E	F	G	H	I	J
Age, x	63	12	34	81	51	14	45	74	24	89
Maintenance costs, y	111	25	41	181	64	21	51	145	43	241

(a) Plot a scatter diagram of these data.

(b) Calculate, to 3 decimal places, the product-moment correlation coefficient. (You may use $\sum x^2 = 30\,625$, $\sum y^2 = 135\,481$, $\sum xy = 62\,412$.) Comment on your value of r.

27 Over a period of time a garage records the number of second-hand cars sold per week (y), and the amount spent on advertising in the local paper (x). The table shows the data collected for 10 weeks picked at random from one year's figures.

Week	A	B	C	D	E	F	G	H	I	J
Expenditure (£x)	360	250	410	560	200	680	710	350	400	430
Cars sold (y)	13	12	17	20	9	21	23	12	17	16

(a) Calculate S_{xy} and S_{xx}.

(b) Find the equation of the regression line.

(c) Give an interpretation of the coefficients in your equation.

(d) Estimate the number of cars likely to be sold if £300 is spent on advertising.

28 In a factory, the packets of oats produced are supposed to contain 1 kg of oats each. Over a long period it has been found that the weights of the contents of the packets of oats produced in the factory are normally distributed with mean 1.02 kg and standard deviation 0.009 kg.

Calculate, to one decimal place, the percentage of packets in the production which have contents whose weights are not within 0.005 kg of the required 1 kg. [E]

29 Jam is packed in tins of nominal net weight 1 kg. The actual weight of jam delivered to a tin by the filling machine is normally distributed about the mean weight set on the machine with a standard deviation of 12 g. The average filling of jam is 1 kg.

(a) Calculate the probability that a tin chosen at random contains less than 985 kg.

It is a legal requirement that no more than 1% of tins contain less than the nominal weight.

(b) Calculate the minimum setting of the filling machine which will meet this requirement. [E]

30 A company monitored the number of days (x) of business trips taken by executives of the company and the corresponding claims (£y) they submitted to cover the total expenditure of these trips.

A random sample of 10 trips gave the following results.

x (days)	10	3	8	17	5	9	14	16	21	13
y (£)	116	39	85	159	61	94	143	178	225	134

(a) Plot these data on a scatter diagram.

Give a reason to support the calculation of a regression line through these points.

(b) Find an equation of the regression line of y on x, in the form $y = a + bx$.

(c) Interpret the slope b and intercept a of your line.

(d) Find the expected expenditure of a trip lasting 11 days.

(e) State, giving a reason, whether or not you would use the line to find the expected expenditure of a trip lasting 2 months. [E]

31 A teacher recorded the following data which refer to the marks gained by 13 children in an aptitude test and a statistics examination.

Child	A	B	C	D	E	F	G	H	I	J	K	L	M
Aptitude test (x)	54	52	42	31	43	23	32	49	37	13	13	36	39
Statistics examination (y)	84	68	71	37	79	58	33	60	47	60	44	64	49

(a) Draw a scatter diagram to represent these two sets of marks.
(b) Calculate, to 3 decimal places, the product-moment correlation coefficient between the test mark and the examination mark.
(c) Comment on your result.   [E]

32 A machine produces sheets of glass of thickness X mm, where $X \sim N(\mu, \sigma^2)$. Over a long period of time it has been found that 2% of the sheets are less than 2 mm thick and 5% of the sheets are more than 3 mm thick. Calculate, to 2 decimal places, the values of μ and σ^2.

33 The random variable X is normally distributed with mean μ and variance σ^2. Given that $P(X > 58.37) = 0.02$ and $P(X < 40.85) = 0.01$, calculate μ and σ^2.   [E]

34 (a) Explain briefly, without doing any algebra, the method by which the principle of least squares can be used to find the equation of a regression line. Show on a sketch the distances whose sum of squares is minimised, and mark clearly which axis records the response (dependent) variable and which the explanatory (independent) variable.

The consumption, in millions of gallons of beer, in a certain country for the years 1976 to 1983 is shown:

Year	1976	1977	1978	1979	1980	1981	1982	1983
Consumption	31	33.7	33.8	35.2	39.3	43.3	42.6	45.1

(b) Draw a scatter diagram to represent these data.
(c) Calculate the equation of the regression line of consumption on year, giving the slope to 2 decimal places, and the intercept to the nearest integer. Draw this line on your diagram.

(d) Use your equation to estimate the consumption for 1984. In making this estimate, state any assumptions which you are making. [E]

35 For 12 consecutive months a factory manager recorded the number of items produced by the factory and the total cost of their production. The following table summarises the manager's data.

Number of items, x (thousands)	18	36	45	22	69	72	13	33	59	79	10	53
Production cost, y (£1000)	37	54	63	42	84	91	33	49	79	98	32	71

(a) Draw a scatter diagram for the data.

(b) Give a reason to support the use of a regression line $y = a + bx$ as a suitable model for these data.

(c) Obtain the equation of the regression line of y on x for these data, giving a to 3 significant figures.

(d) Give a practical interpretation for a and b.

(e) The selling price of each item produced is £1.60. Find the level of output at which total income and estimated total costs are equal. Give a brief interpretation of this value.

36 Explain briefly what is measured by a correlation coefficient. It is usual to expect that the total number of hours studied (x) in preparation for an examination would have a direct association with the number of marks attained (y) in that examination. The results below are for a sample of 10 students selected at random from a large class.

Hours studied (x)	6	15	7	17	19	3	13	11	10	17
Examination marks (y)	36	67	44	85	89	26	50	63	51	80

(a) Draw a scatter diagram to represent these data.

(b) Calculate, to 2 decimal places, the product-moment correlation coefficient between x and y.

(c) Interpret your result.

(d) Explain how the scatter diagram supports your result in (b).

37 A machine is producing a type of circular gasket. The specifications for the use of these gaskets in the manufacture of a certain make of engine are that the thickness should lie between 5.45 and 5.55 mm, and the diameter should lie between 8.45 and 8.54 mm. The machine is producing the gaskets so that their thicknesses are N(5.5, 0.0004), that is, Normally distributed with mean 5.5 mm and variance 0.0004 mm^2, and their diameters are independently distributed N(8.54, 0.0025).

Calculate, to one decimal place, the percentage of gaskets produced which will not meet:

(a) the specified thickness limits

(b) the specified diameter limits   [E]

38 An experiment was conducted to determine the value of a variable y when another variable x had values $x_1, x_2, \ldots, x_n$. Denoting the observed values of y by $y_1, y_2, \ldots, y_n$, the pairs of values $(x_1, y_1), (x_2, y_2), \ldots (x_n, y_n)$ are plotted on a graph. Describe the method of least squares for fitting a straight line to the plotted points, making a clear statement of the quantity which is minimised by this method.

A large field of maize was divided into six plots of equal area and each plot fertilised with a different concentration of fertiliser. The yield of maize from each plot is shown below.

Concentration (oz m^{-2})	0	1	2	3	4	5
Yield (tonnes)	15	22	31	40	48	54

(a) Draw a scatter diagram for these data.

(b) Obtain the equation of the regression line for yield on concentration, giving the values of the coefficients to 2 decimal places.

(c) Use the regression line to obtain a value for the yield when the concentration is 3 oz m^{-2}. State precisely what is being estimated by this value.

(d) State any reservations you would have about making an estimate from the regression equation of the expected yield per plot if 7 oz m^{-2} of fertiliser are applied.   [E]

39 (a) State the quantity that is minimised when using the method of least squares. Use a sketch to illustrate your answer.

The heat output of wood is known to vary with the percentage moisture content. The table below shows, in suitable units, the data obtained from an experiment carried out to assess this variation.

Percentage moisture content (x)	50	8	34	22	45	15	74	82	60	30
Heat output (y)	5.5	7.4	6.2	6.8	5.5	7.1	4.4	3.9	4.9	6.3

(b) Obtain the equation of the regression line for heat output on percentage moisture content, giving the values of the coefficients to 2 decimal places.

(c) Use your equation to estimate the heat output of wood with 40% moisture content. State any reservations you would have about making an estimate from the regression equation of the heat output for a 90% moisture content.

(d) Explain briefly the main implication of your analysis for a person wishing to use wood as a form of heating.   [E]

40 If L has the distribution N(3, 16) find $P(2 \leqslant L \leqslant 5)$.

Examination style paper

S1

---

1. A running club records the number of kilometres, x, to the nearest kilometre, run in training by all of its 90 members. The results are summarized as follows

$$\sum x = 2\,430 \qquad \sum x^2 = 67\,050$$

(a) Calculate the mean μ and the standard deviation σ of the number of kilometres run by members of the club in training.
A new member applies to join the club and she has run μ kilometres in training.
(b) Explain how the mean and standard deviation will be affected if she were to join the club.

(8)

2. In a particular co-educational school 55% of the pupils are girls and 45% are boys. During a games afternoon 65% of the pupils play tennis whilst the remainder are engaged in other activities. Only 40% of the boys play tennis.
A pupil is selected at random, find the probability that:
(a) the pupil is a girl who plays tennis
(b) the pupil is a boy who does not play tennis
(c) the pupil is a girl *given that* the pupil plays tennis.

(8)

3. Steel bolts of circular cross section are to be produced. The lengths of the bolts have to lie between 64.5 and 65.4 mm, and their diameters have to be between 5.5 and 6.0 mm. A machine produces these bolts so that their lengths are normally distributed with a mean of 65.4 mm and a standard deviation of 0.5 mm and their diameters are independently normally distributed about a mean of 5.7 mm with standard deviation σ.
(a) If 1000 bolts are made, how many bolts will not be within the specified limits for length?
(b) If 50 bolts have a diameter greater than 6.0 mm, what is the value of σ?

(11)

4. A group of children sat a Mathematics test and a Verbal Reasoning test. Their results are as follows, where x represents their Mathematics score and y their Verbal Reasoning score.

x	21	4	12	15	11	13	17	29	15	15
y	39	30	22	28	25	37	20	45	32	34

(a) Calculate the value of the product-moment correlation coefficient, r, between x and y.

(You may use $\sum x^2 = 2696$, $\sum y^2 = 10\,288$, $\sum xy = 5014$)

A school uses both of these tests to assess new pupils when they join. A parent governor has suggested that asking the pupils to do two tests is too much and the school should consider using just one test. In response to this suggestion the headteacher said that the school would like to keep both tests as they measure different abilities.

(b) Assess the headteacher's comment in the light of the calculation in part (a).

(14)

5. Over a period of time a publishing house records the sales, y thousand, of 10 similar textbooks, and the amount, £x hundred, spent on advertising each book. The following table shows the data for the 10 books.

x	0.75	3.90	1.65	1.60	4.40	3.05	3.55	2.65	0.45	2.00
y	2.00	5.35	3.00	2.40	5.95	4.50	4.60	3.65	1.30	3.25

(a) Find the equation of the regression line of y on x, giving the coefficients to 2 decimal places.

(You may use $\sum x^2 = 73.5450$; $\sum y^2 = 149.7700$; $\sum xy = 104.1475$)

(b) Give an interpretation of the coefficients in your equation.

(c) Estimate the number of textbooks sold if the publisher spends £375 on advertising.

For a set of novels, the publisher found the sales and advertising to be related by the equation

$$(y - 3.6) = 0.25(x - 2.4)$$

(d) Re-write the equation of the regression line in (a) in the form $(y - \bar{y}) = m(x - \bar{x})$ and compare the effect of advertising on the sales of textbooks and novels.

(15)

6. Three swimmers Alan, Diane and Gopal record the number of lengths of the swimming pool they swim during each practice session over several weeks. The stem and leaf diagram below shows the results for Alan.

Lengths		2 0 means 20
2	0 1 2 2	(4)
2	5 5 6 7 7 8 9	(7)
3	0 1 2 2 4	(5)
3	5 6 6 7 9	(5)
4	0 1 3 3 3 3 3 3 3 4 4 4 4 4 4	(15)
4	5 6 6 8	(4)
5	1	(1)
5	5 6	(2)
6	1 2	(2)
6	7	(1)

    (a) Find the quartiles for Alan's results.

    The table below summarises the results for Diane and Gopal. There are no outliers.

	Diane	Gopal
Smallest value	35	25
Lower quartile	39	35
Median	42	42
Upper quartile	53	49
Largest value	65	57

    An outlier is an observation that falls either more than 1.5 × (interquartile range) above the upper quartile or more than 1.5 × (interquartile range) below the lower quartile.

    (b) Using the same scale and on the same sheet of graph paper draw box plots to represent the data for Alan, Diane and Gopal.

    (c) What inferences can be drawn from a comparison of the three box plots?

    (19)

Appendix

Table 1 The normal distribution function

The function tabulated below is $\Phi(z)$, defined as $\quad \Phi(z) = \dfrac{1}{\sqrt{2\pi}} \displaystyle\int_{-\infty}^{z} e^{-\frac{1}{2}t^2}\, dt.$

z	$\Phi(z)$	z	$\Phi(z)$	z	$\Phi(z)$	z	$\Phi(z)$	z	$\Phi(z)$
0.00	0.5000	0.50	0.6915	1.00	0.8413	1.50	0.9332	2.00	0.9772
0.01	0.5040	0.51	0.6950	1.01	0.8438	1.51	0.9345	2.02	0.9783
0.02	0.5080	0.52	0.6985	1.02	0.8461	1.52	0.9357	2.04	0.9793
0.03	0.5120	0.53	0.7019	1.03	0.8485	1.53	0.9370	2.06	0.9803
0.04	0.5160	0.54	0.7054	1.04	0.8508	1.54	0.9382	2.08	0.9812
0.05	0.5199	0.55	0.7088	1.05	0.8531	1.55	0.9394	2.10	0.9821
0.06	0.5239	0.56	0.7123	1.06	0.8554	1.56	0.9406	2.12	0.9830
0.07	0.5279	0.57	0.7157	1.07	0.8577	1.57	0.9418	2.14	0.9838
0.08	0.5319	0.58	0.7190	1.08	0.8599	1.58	0.9429	2.16	0.9846
0.09	0.5359	0.59	0.7224	1.09	0.8621	1.59	0.9441	2.18	0.9854
0.10	0.5398	0.60	0.7257	1.10	0.8643	1.60	0.9452	2.20	0.9861
0.11	0.5438	0.61	0.7291	1.11	0.8665	1.61	0.9463	2.22	0.9868
0.12	0.5478	0.62	0.7324	1.12	0.8686	1.62	0.9474	2.24	0.9875
0.13	0.5517	0.63	0.7357	1.13	0.8708	1.63	0.9484	2.26	0.9881
0.14	0.5557	0.64	0.7389	1.14	0.8729	1.64	0.9495	2.28	0.9887
0.15	0.5596	0.65	0.7422	1.15	0.8749	1.65	0.9505	2.30	0.9893
0.16	0.5636	0.66	0.7454	1.16	0.8770	1.66	0.9515	2.32	0.9898
0.17	0.5675	0.67	0.7486	1.17	0.8790	1.67	0.9525	2.34	0.9904
0.18	0.5714	0.68	0.7517	1.18	0.8810	1.68	0.9535	2.36	0.9909
0.19	0.5753	0.69	0.7549	1.19	0.8830	1.69	0.9545	2.38	0.9913
0.20	0.5793	0.70	0.7580	1.20	0.8849	1.70	0.9554	2.40	0.9918
0.21	0.5832	0.71	0.7611	1.21	0.8869	1.71	0.9564	2.42	0.9922
0.22	0.5871	0.72	0.7642	1.22	0.8888	1.72	0.9573	2.44	0.9927
0.23	0.5910	0.73	0.7673	1.23	0.8907	1.73	0.9582	2.46	0.9931
0.24	0.5948	0.74	0.7704	1.24	0.8925	1.74	0.9591	2.48	0.9934
0.25	0.5987	0.75	0.7734	1.25	0.8944	1.75	0.9599	2.50	0.9938
0.26	0.6026	0.76	0.7764	1.26	0.8962	1.76	0.9608	2.55	0.9946
0.27	0.6064	0.77	0.7794	1.27	0.8980	1.77	0.9616	2.60	0.9953
0.28	0.6103	0.78	0.7823	1.28	0.8997	1.78	0.9625	2.65	0.9960
0.29	0.6141	0.79	0.7852	1.29	0.9015	1.79	0.9633	2.70	0.9965
0.30	0.6179	0.80	0.7881	1.30	0.9032	1.80	0.9641	2.75	0.9970
0.31	0.6217	0.81	0.7910	1.31	0.9049	1.81	0.9649	2.80	0.9974
0.32	0.6255	0.82	0.7939	1.32	0.9066	1.82	0.9656	2.85	0.9978
0.33	0.6293	0.83	0.7967	1.33	0.9082	1.83	0.9664	2.90	0.9981
0.34	0.6331	0.84	0.7995	1.34	0.9099	1.84	0.9671	2.95	0.9984
0.35	0.6368	0.85	0.8023	1.35	0.9115	1.85	0.9678	3.00	0.9987
0.36	0.6406	0.86	0.8051	1.36	0.9131	1.86	0.9686	3.05	0.9989
0.37	0.6443	0.87	0.8078	1.37	0.9147	1.87	0.9693	3.10	0.9990
0.38	0.6480	0.88	0.8106	1.38	0.9162	1.88	0.9699	3.15	0.9992
0.39	0.6517	0.89	0.8133	1.39	0.9177	1.89	0.9706	3.20	0.9993
0.40	0.6554	0.90	0.8159	1.40	0.9192	1.90	0.9713	3.25	0.9994
0.41	0.6591	0.91	0.8186	1.41	0.9207	1.91	0.9719	3.30	0.9995
0.42	0.6628	0.92	0.8212	1.42	0.9222	1.92	0.9726	3.35	0.9996
0.43	0.6664	0.93	0.8238	1.43	0.9236	1.93	0.9732	3.40	0.9997
0.44	0.6700	0.94	0.8264	1.44	0.9251	1.94	0.9738	3.50	0.9998
0.45	0.6736	0.95	0.8289	1.45	0.9265	1.95	0.9744	3.60	0.9998
0.46	0.6772	0.96	0.8315	1.46	0.9279	1.96	0.9750	3.70	0.9999
0.47	0.6808	0.97	0.8340	1.47	0.9292	1.97	0.9756	3.80	0.9999
0.48	0.6844	0.98	0.8365	1.48	0.9306	1.98	0.9761	3.90	1.0000
0.49	0.6879	0.99	0.8389	1.49	0.9319	1.99	0.9767	4.00	1.0000
0.50	0.6915	1.00	0.8413	1.50	0.9332	2.00	0.9772		

Table 2 Percentage points of the normal distribution

The values z in the table are those which a random variable $Z \sim N(0, 1)$ exceeds with probability p; that is, $P(Z > z) = 1 - \Phi(z) = p$.

p	z	p	z
0.5000	0.0000	0.0500	1.6449
0.4000	0.2533	0.0250	1.9600
0.3000	0.5244	0.0100	2.3263
0.2000	0.8416	0.0050	2.5758
0.1500	1.0364	0.0010	3.0902
0.1000	1.2816	0.0005	3.2905

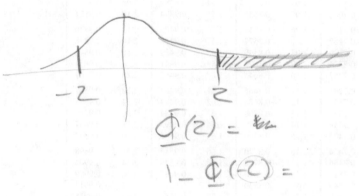

Answers

Exercise 2A

1

Temp. (°C)	Tally	Frequency
18					3
19								6
20															13
21											9
22												10
23						4
24								6
25							5
26				2
27					3

2

Rating	Tally	Frequency
A	|||||	5
B	||||| ||||| ||||| ||	17
C	||||| ||||| |||||	14
D	||||| ||||	9
E	|||||	5

3

```
4 | 0 1 1 1 1 1 2 2 2 2 4 4 5 6 7 8 9
5 | 0 0 1 1 2 4 4 5 8 9 9
6 | 2 5 6 7 7 7 8 9 9 9
7 | 0 1 2 2 3 3 7 8 8
8 | 0 0 2 4 4 5 5 6 6 8 9 9 9
```

4

```
0 | 8 9 9
1 | 0 0 2 2 3 4 5 5 6 7 7 7 7 8 9 9 9 9
2 | 0 1 1 1 2 2 3 3 3 6 6 6 6 7 8 8 8
3 | 0 0 0 1 2 3 4 6 6 7
4 | 3 5
```

5 Length in cm   2|2 means 2.2

```
2 | 2 5 5 7 7
3 | 1 2 2 4 5 5 5 7 8 8
4 | 3 3 7 7 8
5 | 1 1 2 2 2 2 6 8
6 | 1 1 2 4 4 4 6 6 7 8
7 | 1 2 3 5 5 5 5 6 6 7 8 8
8 | 1 3 3 4 6 6 8 8 9
```

6

```
1 | 0 4 4 5 6 7 7 9 9
2 | 0 1 1 2 5 5 5 5 8 8 9 9 9
3 | 1 2 3 4 5 5 6 7 8 8 8 9
4 | 2 3 4 4 4 5 5 6 6 7 8 9 9
5 | 1 1 1 2 2 2 3 4 5 6 7 7 7 9
```

7

		1994			1993

```
                    8 7 5 4 2 2 2 2 1 0 0 │ 3 │
9 9 8 8 7 7 7 7 5 5 5 3 3 3 3 3 2 2 0 0 │ 4 │ 0 1 1 1 1 1 2 2 2 2 4 4 5 6 7 8 9
                          6 6 4 2 2 2 0 0 │ 5 │ 0 0 1 1 2 4 4 5 8 9 9
                        9 6 6 3 3 3 2 0 0 │ 6 │ 2 5 6 7 7 7 8 9 9 9
                            7 6 6 3 2 1 0 │ 7 │ 0 1 2 2 3 3 7 8 8
                                          │ 8 │ 0 0 2 4 4 5 5 6 6 8 9 9 9
```

Marks in 1994 are generally lower than in 1993.

8

	Girls			Boys

```
9 8 8 6 6 6 3 3 1 1 1 0 0 │ 1 │ 0 1 4 7 7 9
      9 9 8 7 7 6 5 5 4 3 1 │ 2 │ 0 0 0 2 2 4 5 6 6 8 8 8 9
        9 8 6 5 4 3 2 2 1 0 │ 3 │ 1 2 2 4 4 6 7 8 9
              8 4 4 3 2 1 0 │ 4 │ 0 1 1 2 2 2 2 4 6 7 8 9
```

Boys buy slightly more packets than girls.

Exercise 2B

1 (a) 5.5, 7.5; 6.5; 2   (b) −0.5, 2.5; 1; 3
  (c) 4.5, 14.5; 9.5; 10   (d) −8.5, −1.5; −5; 7
  (e) 1.495, 1.755, 1.625, 0.26

2

Classes	0–9	10–19	20–29	30–39	40–49	50–59	60–69	70–79
Frequency	10	4	5	12	7	5	5	2

3 Reveals patterns; allows summaries to be made. Some detail lost.

4

Class	60–64	65–69	70–74	75–79	80–84	85–89	90–94	95–99
Frequency	9	6	5	7	6	9	4	4

5

No. of pairs	30–39	40–49	50–59	60–69	70–79	80–89	90–99
No. of Fridays	1	5	9	17	12	3	5

6

Time (hours)	650–659	660–669	670–679	680–689	690–699	700–709	710–719	720–729	730–739
Frequency	1	3	3	7	15	7	7	4	3

7 (a) Height is a continuous variable

(b) For each bar, and hence the whole histogram, area is proportional to frequency

(c)

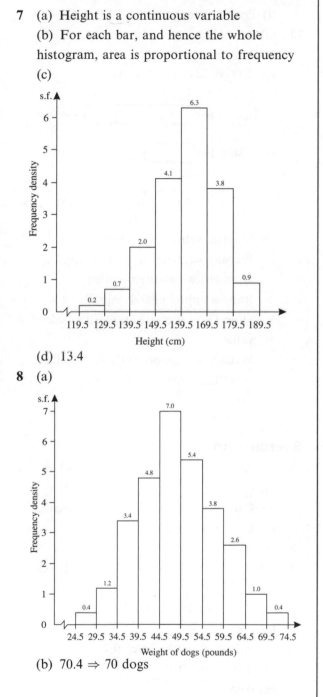

(d) 13.4

8 (a)

(b) 70.4 ⇒ 70 dogs

9 (a)

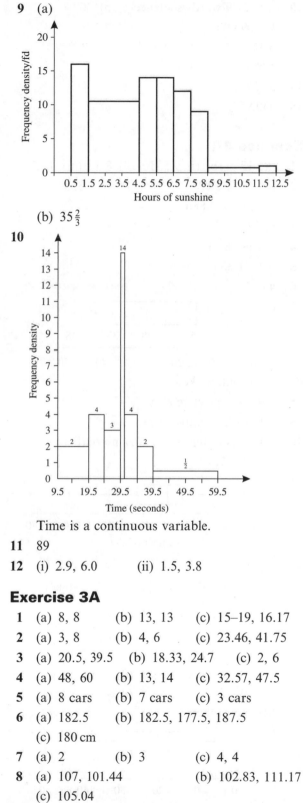

(b) $35\frac{2}{3}$

10

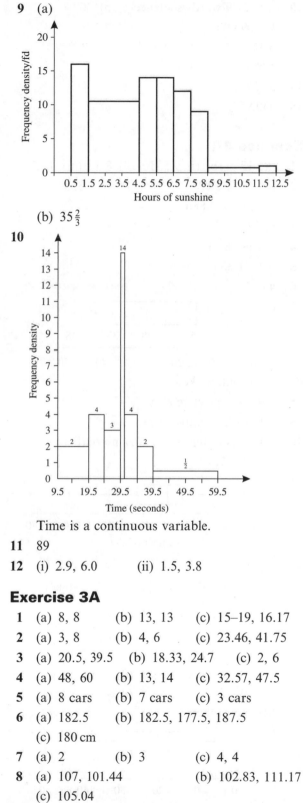

Time is a continuous variable.

11 89

12 (i) 2.9, 6.0   (ii) 1.5, 3.8

Exercise 3A

1 (a) 8, 8   (b) 13, 13   (c) 15–19, 16.17

2 (a) 3, 8   (b) 4, 6   (c) 23.46, 41.75

3 (a) 20.5, 39.5   (b) 18.33, 24.7   (c) 2, 6

4 (a) 48, 60   (b) 13, 14   (c) 32.57, 47.5

5 (a) 8 cars   (b) 7 cars   (c) 3 cars

6 (a) 182.5   (b) 182.5, 177.5, 187.5

(c) 180 cm

7 (a) 2   (b) 3   (c) 4, 4

8 (a) 107, 101.44   (b) 102.83, 111.17

(c) 105.04

9 44, 35, 55

10 (a) 21.9 words/sentence   (b) 30.08

11 £13 094.60

12 3.34

13 5.689 peas/pod

14 39.37

15 630.95

Exercise 4A

1 (a) 17   (b) (i) 9.5, 18 (ii) 8.5   (iii) 4.25

2 (a) 17.6, 3.627   (b) 14.49, 1.353
   (c) 21.46, 4.886

3 6, 3.667

4 147.94, 88.15

5 6.25, 1.333

6 4.6, 2

7 (a)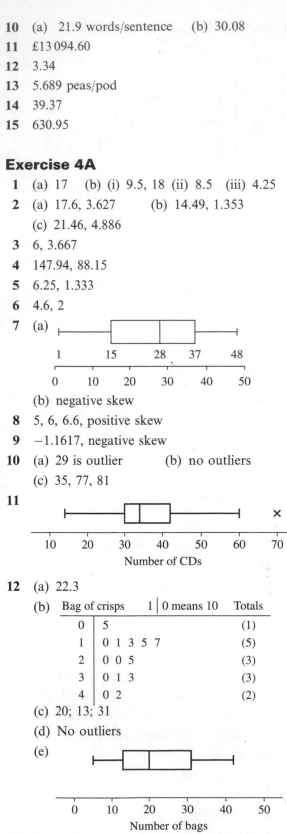

   (b) negative skew

8 5, 6, 6.6, positive skew

9 −1.1617, negative skew

10 (a) 29 is outlier   (b) no outliers
   (c) 35, 77, 81

11

12 (a) 22.3

   (b)

Bag of crisps	1 | 0 means 10	Totals
0	5	(1)
1	0 1 3 5 7	(5)
2	0 0 5	(3)
3	0 1 3	(3)
4	0 2	(2)

   (c) 20; 13; 31

   (d) No outliers

   (e)

Number of bags

(f) Positive skew since $Q_3 - Q_2 > Q_2 - Q_1$

13 (a) 805; 621

   (b) 650, 665

   (c) 2100 & 2315 are outliers

   (d)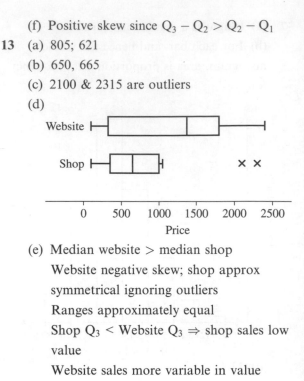

   (e) Median website > median shop
   Website negative skew; shop approx
   symmetrical ignoring outliers
   Ranges approximately equal
   Shop Q_3 < Website $Q_3 \Rightarrow$ shop sales low
   value
   Website sales more variable in value
   $IQR_w > IQR_s$

Exercise 5A

1 (a) $\frac{8}{15}$ (b) $\frac{1}{5}$ (c) $\frac{17}{30}$ (d) $\frac{3}{10}$

2 (a) $\frac{1}{52}$ (b) $\frac{4}{13}$ (c) $\frac{49}{52}$ (d) $\frac{3}{52}$
   (e) Card is a diamond but not a queen.
   (f) Card is not a diamond and not a queen.

3 0.3

4 (a) 0.1   (b) 0.2   (c) $\frac{1}{2}$ (d) 0.2
   (e) 0.8   (f) $\frac{1}{2}$

5 (a) 0.1   (b) 0.25   (c) 0.5   (d) 0.25
   (e) 0.85

6 (a) 0.2   (b) 0.4   (c) 0.4   (d) 0.2

7 (a) 0.10   (b) 0.05

8 (a) 0.45

9 (a) 0.05

10 (a) $Y \cap F'$ means that the carburettor is made
   in factory Y and is not faulty.
   $Y \cup Z$ means that the carburettor is made in
   factory Y or factory Z.
   (b) 0.009, 0.012, 0.0075   (d) 0.0285

Exercise 5B

1 (a) $\frac{1}{3}$ (b) $\frac{8}{15}$ (c) $\frac{2}{3}$

2 (a) 0.1   (b) 0.7

3 (a) (i) 0.175 (ii) $\frac{9}{20}$ (b) Cereal and coffee

4 (a) 0.3   (b) $\frac{3}{4}$ (c) $\frac{3}{7}$ (d) $\frac{2}{3}$

5 (a) 0.46   (b) 0.652 (c) 0.348 (d) $\frac{4}{9}$

6 (a) 0.3375   (b) 0.2225   (c) 0.434

7 (a) $\frac{23}{30}$ (b) $\frac{4}{15}$ (c) $\frac{3}{4}$

8 (a) $\frac{1}{2}, \frac{1}{8}$ (b) $\frac{1}{4} = P(A)$

9 (a) 0.395   (b) 0.089   (c) 0.107

10 (a) 0.33   (b) $\frac{7}{11}$

11 $\frac{13}{25}, \frac{3}{4}$

12 (a) $\frac{7}{15}$ (b) $\frac{4}{15}$ (c) $\frac{4}{15}, \frac{119}{450}$

Exercise 5C

1 (a) 0.42   (b) 0.88

2 0.58

3 0.94

4 (a) $\frac{1}{6}, \frac{1}{9}, \frac{1}{6}, 0, 0, \frac{1}{36}$ (b) B (c) C

5 (a) $\frac{4}{15}$ (b) $\frac{2}{5}$ (c) $\frac{2}{3}$ (d) $\frac{3}{5}$
    (e) H = hard-back and F = fiction

6 (a) 0.65   (b) 0.7   (c) 0.35

7 (a) 0.1   (b) 0.2   (c) 0.5

8 (a) $\frac{1}{2}$ (b) $\frac{1}{3}$ (c) $\frac{1}{2}$ (d) $\frac{2}{3}$
    (e) $\frac{1}{3}$ (f) 0   (g) $\frac{1}{6}$ (h) R and Q'

10 (a) 0.2   (b) 0.03   (c) 0.32

11 (a) $\frac{10}{49}$ (b) $\frac{4}{21}$ $8 \rightarrow \frac{1}{7}$; $7,8,9 \rightarrow \frac{1}{7}$

12 (a) Independence   (b) Mutually exclusive
    (c) Mutually exclusive   (d) 0   (e) $\frac{1}{6}$

13 (a) $\frac{1}{8}$ (b) $\frac{3}{11}$

14 $\frac{15}{44}$; not; $\frac{1}{10}$

Exercise 5D

1 (a) $\frac{5}{91}$ (b) $\frac{15}{182}$ (c) $\frac{45}{182}$

2 (a) $\frac{125}{324}$ (b) $\frac{25}{216}$ (c) $\frac{1}{36}$

3 (a) $\frac{1}{114}$ (b) $\frac{7}{114}$ (c) $\frac{14}{57}$

4 (a) 0.57   (b) $\frac{1}{19}$ (c) 0.0974

5 (a) (i) $\frac{17}{32}$ (ii) $\frac{17}{80}$ (iii) $\frac{63}{80}$ (iv) $\frac{34}{59}$
    (b) (i) 0.0485 (ii) 0.4448 (iii) 0.0634

Exercise 5E

1 (b) $\frac{4}{10}$ (c) $\frac{6}{10}$
    (d) R_2 independent of G_1 and Y_1

2 (a) $\frac{3}{4}$ (b) $\frac{1}{2}$

3 (a) $\frac{1}{26}$ (b) $\frac{1}{13}$ (c) $\frac{12}{13}$

4 (a) $\frac{2}{15}$ (b) $\frac{2}{9}$ (c) $\frac{22}{45}$

5 (a)

    (b) $\frac{3}{10}$ (c) $\frac{7}{30}$

6 (a) $\frac{2}{15}$ (b) $\frac{2}{3}$ (c) 0   (d) 1

7 (a) $\frac{1}{5}$ (b) $\frac{3}{5}$ (c) $\frac{1}{5}$

8 (a) $\frac{1}{10}$ (b) $\frac{2}{5}$ (c) $\frac{1}{2}$ (d) $\frac{3}{4}$ (e) $\frac{1}{4}$
    (f) not independent

9 (b) $\frac{5}{9}$ (c) $\frac{1}{5}$

10 (a) $\frac{31}{90}$ (b) $\frac{6}{31}$ (c) unlikely

11 (a) $\frac{7}{10}$ (b) $\frac{3}{10}$ (c) $\frac{1}{10}$

Review exercise 1

1 480

2 (a) 80   (b) 30   (c) 250

3 $\frac{1}{2}$

4 10.8, −0.019

5 (a) 25   (b) 19   (c) 37
    (d) (i) $\frac{25}{37}$ (ii) $\frac{19}{37}$ (iii) $\frac{7}{37}$ (iv) $\frac{7}{19}$

6 (a) mutually exclusive
    (b) all of B in A
    (c) some members of C in D

7 (a) 5, 8, 10, 5, 1   (b) 29
    (c) 31   (d) 22, 38

9 5.75

10 3.85

11 X is symmetric, the inter-quartile range of Y is
    much smaller than that of X.

12 median 3, mean 3.19, s.d. 1.3

13 $\frac{8}{15}$

14 (a) 115   (b) $\frac{7}{115}, \frac{13}{115}, \frac{20}{51}$

15 It is easy to compare quartiles, skews, etc.

16 (a) $\frac{3}{20}$ (b) $\frac{2}{3}$

(c) e.g. $P(\bar{B}) = \frac{2}{3} = P(\bar{B}|M)$, thus they are independent.

17 (a) $Q_1 = 252$, $Q_2 = 261.7$, $Q_3 = 297.2$

(b) whiskers at 220.6 and 362.3, box from 252 to 297.2

(c) 362.3 possible outlier

(d) mean = £272: standard deviation = £35.30

(e) (i) standard deviation would decrease

(ii) interquartile range is unchanged

18 (a) $\frac{4}{15}$ (b) $\frac{3}{4}$

It is unlikely that a golfer will choose a club at random knowing which suits particular shots.

19 (a) $x = 288.4$ $S_y^2 = 4.2915$ $S_x^2 = 429.1566$

(b) Take a large sample; use raw data.

20 (a) 11, 9, 8, 1

(b) $Q_2 = 14$, $Q_1 = 6$, $Q_3 = 23$

(c) $P_{67} = 21$

(f) Both likely to be late but D could be subject to long delays whereas there is less spread in delay from S. Easier to plan with S, eg. add 30 minutes to each journey time.

21 (a) 2   4   6 (b) $P(\text{obeys}) = \frac{9}{10}$ (c) $\frac{2}{7}$

     5   9 14

     7 13 20

22 mean = 20, standard deviation = 12.5

23 whiskers at 23 and 78, box from 40.9 to 58.1, median marked at 49.0

24 (a) $\frac{11}{15}$ or 0.733 (b) $\frac{3}{8}$ or 0.375

25 (a) 7, 6, 4, 8

(b) $Q_1 = 5.7$, $Q_2 = 6.5$, $Q_3 = 8.1$

(c) whiskers at 5.0 and 9.9

26

0	1	2	3	4	5	6	7	8
2	4	6	9	12	9	8	7	3

27 1.29 m

28

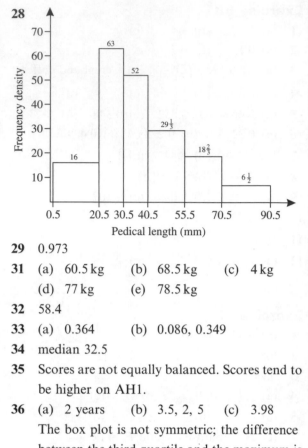

29 0.973

31 (a) 60.5 kg (b) 68.5 kg (c) 4 kg

(d) 77 kg (e) 78.5 kg

32 58.4

33 (a) 0.364 (b) 0.086, 0.349

34 median 32.5

35 Scores are not equally balanced. Scores tend to be higher on AH1.

36 (a) 2 years (b) 3.5, 2, 5 (c) 3.98

The box plot is not symmetric; the difference between the third quartile and the maximum is much larger than that between the first quartile and the minimum

37 205.2 ml, 9.22 ml

38 (a) $P(E \cap F) = P(E)P(F)$

(b) $P(G \cap H) = 0$; $\frac{8}{15}$; $\frac{1}{2}$; $\frac{1}{6}$; yes

39 Positive skew

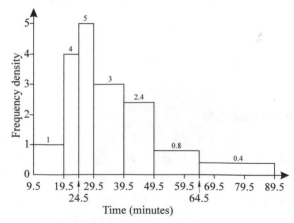

40 (a) 51.06, 35.44, 58.43 (b) 41.06, 55.89
(c) 25.03, 69.41

41 (a) Group B
(b) 4 years 8 months, 3 years 2 month

42 $\frac{1}{5}; \frac{1}{6}, \frac{1}{3}$

43 $\frac{1}{2}$; independent

44 (a) 755 hours, 744.3 hours, 761.2 hours
(b) mean 751.2, s.d = 15.9, skew = −0.7
(c) negative skew

45

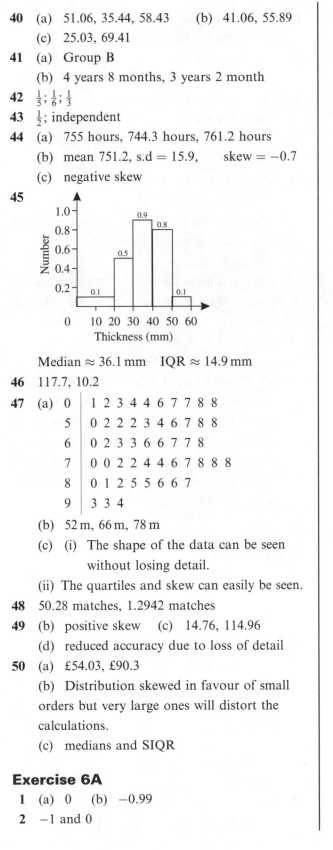

Median ≈ 36.1 mm IQR ≈ 14.9 mm

46 117.7, 10.2

47 (a)

0	1 2 3 4 4 6 7 7 8 8
5	0 2 2 2 3 4 6 7 8 8
6	0 2 3 3 6 6 7 7 8
7	0 0 2 2 4 4 6 7 8 8 8
8	0 1 2 5 5 6 6 7
9	3 3 4

(b) 52 m, 66 m, 78 m
(c) (i) The shape of the data can be seen without losing detail.
(ii) The quartiles and skew can easily be seen.

48 50.28 matches, 1.2942 matches

49 (b) positive skew (c) 14.76, 114.96
(d) reduced accuracy due to loss of detail

50 (a) £54.03, £90.3
(b) Distribution skewed in favour of small orders but very large ones will distort the calculations.
(c) medians and SIQR

Exercise 6A

1 (a) 0 (b) −0.99

2 −1 and 0

3 (i) −1 and 1 (ii) 0

4 (a) $r = 0.577...[S_{xy} = 620,$
$S_{yy} = 826, S_{xx} = 1396.83]$
(b) $r = 0.108...[S_{xy} = 88.516,$
$S_{yy} = 646.902, S_{xx} = 1034.509]$
(c) $r = 0.481...[S_{xy} = 6.2886,$
$S_{yy} = 38.989, S_{xx} = 4.3759]$

5 (a) $r = 0.9739...[S_{xy} = 56.935,$
$S_{yy} = 223.135, S_{xx} = 15.315]$
(b) $r = -0.974...[S_{xy} = -5342.64,$
$S_{yy} = 860.727, S_{xx} = 34\,936.19]$

6 (a) $r = 0.951...$
(b) $r = -0.978...$
(c) $r = 0.7602...$

7 (a) $S_{xx} = 10.857\,14, S_{yy} = 28, S_{xy} = -17,$
$r = -0.975...$

8 (a) (i) none (ii) none
(b) $r = 0.9417...$ On this evidence we can support the statement.
$[S_{xy} = 1029.286, S_{yy} = 745.714,$
$S_{xx} = 1601.714]..$

9 (a) $S_{xx} = 19.1819, S_{yy} = 172\,234.9,$
$S_{xy} = 1231.27, r = 0.677...$
(b) There is some evidence to show that the taller you are the more you weigh.

10 (a) $S_{xx} = 1.2889..., S_{yy} = 8.316\,01,$
$S_{xy} = -1.828..., r = -0.558...$
(b) There is minimal evidence to suggest that as unemployment increases wage inflation decreases.

11 (a) $r = 0.4726...$ (b) $r = 0.4663...$
There is slight evidence to suggest that blood pressure rises as weight and age increase.

12 (b) (i) $S_{tp} = 255$ (ii) $r = 0.9354...$

13 $r = 0.8349...[S_{xx} = 82.5, S_{yy} = 32.900,$
$S_{xy} = 43.5]$
There is some evidence of linear relationship. The older the trainee the longer it is likely to take to train him/her.

14 (b) $r = 0.685$

15 (a) $r = -0.744$

(b) Sales in one shop do tend to be affected by sales in the other. If sales are up in one shop they are fairly likely to be down in the other. This suggests there is an overlap of clients.

Exercise 7A

1 (a) 16.2 is the length of the spring with no mass attached.

(b) 0.04 is the increase in spring length for every gram increase in the mass suspended.

(c) 46.2

2 (a) £10 250   (b) £750   (c) £17 750

(d) Yes. Under the new company scheme he should get £32 750 p.a.

(e) The company has only been running for 30 years so only has 30 years of real data. It is very questionable whether the formula is suitable for employees with more than 30 years employment with the firm.

3 $S_{xy} = 69.6, S_{xx} = 40.8,$
$y = 1.7059x - 0.2941$

4 $S_{xy} = 14.5, S_{xx} = 10, y = 1.45x - 0.07$

5 (a) $\bar{x} = 10, \bar{y} = 110.2, S_{xy} = 86, S_{xx} = 40$
$y - 110.2 = 2.15(x - 10)$ or $y = 2.15x + 88.7$

6 (a) negative linear

(b) $S_{xy} = -280, S_{xx} = 2800, \bar{y} = 12.9714,$
$\bar{x} = 40, y = 16.9714 - 0.1x$

7 $S_{HT} = 9.664, S_{TT} = 6.12,$
$H = 1.58T - 11.03,$
$H = 1.3$ when $T = 7.8$

8 (a) Linear relationship, number of items fixed

(b) $S_{xy} = 6344, S_{xx} = 6486, \bar{y} = 65,$
$\bar{x} = 45, y = 0.978x + 20.985$

(c) 17174; break-even point

9 (a) $S_{xy} = -3243.533, S_{xx} = 1049.78$
$y = 55.52 - 3.0898x, h = 217.321 - 3.09s$

(b) Every extra rev/min reduces the life of the drill by just over 3 hours.

(c) 124.62 hours

10 $\bar{A} = 5.5, \bar{S} = 0.7732, S = 0.694 + 0.014A,$
0.744

11 $S_{TH} = 1200, S_{TT} = 150\,000,$
$H = 0.008T - 0.8, 0.8$ units

12 (b) $S_{xy} = -1.450\,45, S_{xx} = 136.18$
$y = 0.231 - 0.011x$

13 (a) $S_{xy} = 3477.6, S_{xx} = 4402$
$y = 0.16 + 0.79x$

(b) The amount of extra food per extra hen

(c) £85.37

14 $\bar{T} = 17.5, \bar{A} = 14.875$
$A = 6.30 + 0.49T$
When $T = 20, A = 16.1$. Both observed values have errors in them.
0.49 grams
$T = 0$ is outside the range of the experimental results. This means the value of A would not be reliable.

15 (b) $y = 0.5x + 46.5$

(c) (i) 61.5; 54.5; 71.5; 89

(ii) 30 and 50 are within the range of the data collected so the marks of 61.5 and 71.5 are acceptable. 16 is only just outside the range of the data collected so it is probably acceptable. 85 is well beyond the range of the data collected so the mark of 85 cannot be accepted with any degree of confidence.

Exercise 8A

1 (a) $\frac{1}{12}$ (b) $\frac{3}{4}$

2 (a) $\frac{3}{8}$ (b) $\frac{5}{8}$

3 (a) Yes; $x = \frac{1}{6}$ (b) Yes; $x = 0.2$ (c) No

4 (a) $a = \frac{1}{2}, b = \frac{1}{6}, c = \frac{1}{3}$ (b) $\frac{2}{3}$

5 $P(x = r) = \frac{r}{21}; r = 1, 2, ...6$

6 (b)

s:	2	3	4	5	6	7	8
$P(S = s)$:	$\frac{1}{16}$	$\frac{2}{16}$	$\frac{3}{16}$	$\frac{4}{16}$	$\frac{3}{16}$	$\frac{2}{16}$	$\frac{1}{16}$

(c) $\frac{15}{16}$

(e)

d:	0	1	2	3
$P(D = d)$:	$\frac{4}{16}$	$\frac{6}{16}$	$\frac{4}{16}$	$\frac{2}{16}$

(f) $\frac{6}{16}$ or $\frac{3}{8}$

7 (a)

x:	150	120	70^	40
$P(X = x)$:	$\frac{1}{10}$	$\frac{3}{10}$	$\frac{3}{10}$	$\frac{3}{10}$

8 (b)

t:	1	2	3
$P(T = t)$:	$\frac{1}{2}$	$\frac{1}{4}$	$\frac{1}{4}$

(c)

h:	0	1
$P(H = h)$:	$\frac{1}{8}$	$\frac{7}{8}$

9 (a) (i) Yes; discrete

(ii) No; F not a number

(iii) Yes

(b) (i) No; E not a number

(ii) Yes (iii) Yes (iv) Yes

10 (a) $\frac{5}{7}$

(c)

x:	1	2	3	4	5
$P(X = x)$:	$\frac{3}{7}$	$\frac{1}{7}$	$\frac{1}{7}$	$\frac{1}{7}$	$\frac{1}{7}$

11 (a) $\frac{7}{9}$

(c)

x:	0	1	2	3	4
$P(X = x)$:	$\frac{1}{9}$	$\frac{2}{9}$	$\frac{2}{9}$	$\frac{2}{9}$	$\frac{2}{9}$

12 (a) $k = 1$

(b)

x:	1	2	3
$P(X = x)$:	$\frac{4}{16}$	$\frac{5}{16}$	$\frac{7}{16}$

13 $\frac{1}{32}$

14 (a) 0.128 (b) $P(X = x) = 0.2(0.8)^{x-1}$

(c) 0.512

15 (a) $\frac{2}{15}$ (b) $\frac{7}{15}$

Exercise 8B

1 (a) $E(X) = \frac{11}{6}$ $Var(X) = \frac{17}{36}$

(b) $E(X) = 0$ $Var(X) = 0.5$

(c) $E(X) = -0.5$ $Var(X) = 2.25$

2 $E(Y) = 3.5$ $Var(Y) = \frac{35}{12}$

3 (a)

s:	2	3	4	5	6	7	8	9	10	11	12
$P(S = s)$:	$\frac{1}{36}$	$\frac{2}{36}$	$\frac{3}{36}$	$\frac{4}{36}$	$\frac{5}{36}$	$\frac{6}{36}$	$\frac{5}{36}$	$\frac{4}{36}$	$\frac{3}{36}$	$\frac{2}{36}$	$\frac{1}{36}$

(b) $E(S) = 7$ (c) $Var(S) = \frac{35}{6}$

4 (a)

d:	0	1	2	3	4	5
$P(D = d)$:	$\frac{6}{36}$	$\frac{10}{36}$	$\frac{8}{36}$	$\frac{6}{36}$	$\frac{4}{36}$	$\frac{2}{36}$

(b) $E(D) = \frac{35}{18}$ (c) $Var(D) = \frac{665}{324}$

5 (a) $\frac{91}{6}$ (b) $\frac{140}{3}$

6 (a)

h:	0	1	2
$P(H = h)$:	$\frac{1}{4}$	$\frac{1}{2}$	$\frac{1}{4}$

(b) $E(H) = 1$ (c) $Var(H) = \frac{1}{2}$

7 (b) $E(T) = \frac{7}{4}$ $Var(T) = \frac{11}{16}$ or 0.6875

8 87.5p

9 (a) 2 (b) $a = \frac{3}{8}$ $b = \frac{1}{4}$

10 (a) 1p $\rightarrow \frac{17}{40}$ 2p $\rightarrow -\frac{7}{20}$

(b) Yes with 1p since expected value is positive.

(c) It was making a loss because people saw that 1p was better.

11 (a) $\frac{20}{49}$ (b) $\frac{120}{49}$ (c) 2.5739

12 $\frac{11}{100}$ $E(X) = 0.21$ $Var(X) = 0.2059$

13 (a) $\frac{1}{100}$ (b) 3.54; 0.4684

Exercise 8C

1 (a) 7 (b) -4 (c) 81 (d) 81 (e) 13

(f) 12

2 (a) 3μ (b) $2\mu + 3$ (c) $3 - 2\mu$ (d) $4\sigma^2$

(e) $4\sigma^2$ (f) $\sigma^2 + \mu^2$

3 (a) $a = \frac{1}{5}$, $b = -4$ (b) $a = 3$, $b = 40$

(c) $a = 2$, $b = 10$ (d) $a = 1$, $b = -15$

4 (a)

x:	1	2	3
$P(X = x)$:	$\frac{3}{8}$	$\frac{1}{4}$	$\frac{3}{8}$

(b) 2 (c) $\frac{3}{4}$ (d) 3 (e) 3, $\frac{27}{4}$

5 Sam 90p, Ruth 60p.

6 (a) 0.2 (b) 3.56 (c) 1.1 (d) 0.89

7 (a) 0.35 (b) 4.2

8 $E(R) = \frac{11}{4}$ $Var(R) = \frac{37}{16}$

(a) $E(2R - 5) = \frac{1}{2}$ $Var(2R - 5) = \frac{37}{4}$

(b) $E(R_1 - R_2) = 0$ $Var(R_1 - R_2) = \frac{37}{8}$

Exercise 8D

1 (a) 3.5; $\frac{35}{12}$ (b) $\frac{2}{3}$

2 (a) 10.5; $\frac{399}{12}$ (b) 0.6

3 (a) $\frac{3}{10}$ (b) 11; 33

4 (a) $\frac{3}{10}$ (b) 10; 33

5 Possibly but may cluster towards the centre.

6 Assumes dart aimed at random. Depends on skill of thrower.

7 Yes

8 $P(X = r) = \frac{1}{6}$, $r = 1, ...6$; $3\frac{1}{2}$, $\frac{35}{12}$

Exercise 9A

All values of $\Phi(z)$ are taken from Table 1 on page 197 *without* interpolation.

1 (a) 0.9625 (b) 0.9938 (c) 0.6103

(d) 0.9332 (e) 0.9279 (f) 0.0375

(g) 0.0062   (h) 0.3897   (i) 0.0668
(j) 0.2389

2   (a) 0.2907   (b) 0.0994   (c) 0.383
(d) 0.867   (e) 0.7583   (f) 0.1815

3   (a) 1.64   (b) 0.23   (c) 1.82   (d) 0.31
(e) 1.25   (f) 1.97

4   (a) 0.1056   (b) 0.1587   (c) 0.8185

5   (a) 2, 0.9772   (b) 2, 0.0228   (c) 1.75, 0.4599
(d) −0.67, 0.2512   (e) −0.786, 0.2852
(f) −1, 0.63, 0.577

6   (a) 0.9082   (b) 0.004   (c) 0.4904
(d) 0.2286   (e) 0.7938

7   14.432

8   (a) 4   (b) 200   (c) 100   (d) 2

9   (a) 0.04   (b) 3.1   (c) 3.2   (d) 14

10   (a) $\mu = 1.51, \sigma = 0.051$
(b) $\mu = 51.3, \sigma = 20.5$

11   $\mu = 30, \sigma = 2$

12   4.01%

13   38.2%, 4.46%

14   31.47%

15   0.092

16   12.52 minutes or 12.51 minutes

17   (a) 37.5%   (b) 125.5 hours to 194.5 hours

18   $\mu = 7.548, \sigma = 0.258$

Review exercise 2

1   (b) uniform   (c) 3.5, 1.7078

2   strong positive linear association

3   0.3707

4   0.3231

5   (a) 0.8749   (b) 0.3749

6   no, many other factors might be involved

7   (a) $r = 0$ (b) $r = 1$ (c) $r = -0.9$

8   $O = 1.25 + 0.96M$

9   0.1209

10   (a) 0.7   (b) 2.4   (c) 0.84

11   (a)

x:	−6	−3	0	7	12
P($X = x$):	0.04	0.18	0.54	0.22	0.02

(c) 15.72

12   (a) Discrete uniform or rectangular
(b) 0.4   (c) by symmetry E(x) = 2

13   (a)

x:	−5	−3	−1	2	4	6
P($X = x$):	$\frac{1}{6}$	$\frac{1}{6}$	$\frac{1}{6}$	$\frac{1}{6}$	$\frac{1}{6}$	$\frac{1}{6}$

(b) 0.5   (d) in growth

14   (a) 0.4   (b) 0.8   (c) 2.6   (d) 1.44

15   (a) 0.1056   (b) 0.0124

16   0.3755

17   (b) extra number of fish caught per year
(c) number of fish caught becomes negative
(d) $y = 158 + 28x$
(e) number caught decreases but tends towards constant value
(f) 158 is the long-term expected catch per year

18   (a) 0.9938   (b) 0.0668

19   $E = 0.008T - 2.4, 1.04$ mm

20   (a) x is explanatory, y is response
(b) 0.9792
Strong positive linear association.
As length increases so does width.

21   0.0342

22   (a) 0.9918   (b) 0.1505

23   $r = 0.340$

24   (a) 0.227   (b) 0.54

25   1.514 mm, 0.051 mm

26   (b) $r = 0.937$

27   (a) 6540, 255 450   (b) $y = 0.0256x + 4.863$
(c) 4.863 represents cars likely to be sold with no advertising, 0.0256 represents the increase in car sales per £1 of advertising.
(d) 12.5–13

28   95.5%

29   (a) 0.1056   (b) 1.028 kg

30   (a) x is independent of y
Points are close to a straight line
(b) $y = 8.64 + 9.89x$
(c) Slope – average daily subsistence cost, intercept – average travel cost unrelated to length of trip.
(d) £117.40

(e) 2 months is outside the range of the model so you should not use the line.

31 (b) $r = 0.535$

(c) Some correlation.

32 2.56, 0.0729

33 50.15, 16

34 (c) $c = 2.09x - 4105$ [x is year]

(d) Since you are extrapolating you are assuming no major changes in drinking habits (caused by tax changes, etc.); 41.56

35 (b) points on straight line, x does not depend on y

(c) $y = 0.966x - 20.1$

(d) a – fixed costs (overheads)

b – variable costs (manufacturing costs)

(e) 31 714 break even point

36 (b) $r = 0.961$

(c) strong correlation (the more the hours of study the better the exam marks)

(d) data close to a straight line with positive gradient

37 (a) 1.2%   (b) 53.6%

38 (b) $y = 8.06x + 14.86$ (c) 39.04 tonnes

(d) 7 oz well outside given data. It would be unwise to use the equation to estimate the yield.

39 (a) $\sum$ errors   (b) $y = 7.77 - 0.05x$

(c) 5.8 units

(d) It is better to use wood with a low moisture content.

40 0.29

Examination style paper S1

1 (a) $\mu = 27$, $\sigma = 4$

(b) μ no change; σ reduced

2 (a) 0.47   (b) 0.27   (c) 0.72

3 (a) 536   (b) 0.1824

4 (a) 0.588

(b) Positive correlation suggests one test should do.

5 (a) $y = 0.93 + 1.11x$

(b) 0.93 → without advertising 930 copies would be sold. 1.11 → for every £100 spent on advertising an extra 1110 books are sold,

(c) 5092   (d) $(y - 3.6) = 1.11(x - 2.4)$

1.11 > 0.25 and 0.93 < 3.00 → novels sell better without advertising than textbooks but the sale of textbooks increases more for every £100 spent on advertising.

6 (a) 30; 42; 44

(b)

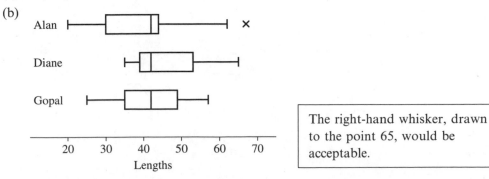

The right-hand whisker, drawn to the point 65, would be acceptable.

(c) Alan   Diane   Gopal
     −ve skew   +ve skew   Symmetrical
                   All same median
                   All same IQR

Any other comment, eg: Diane tends to swim more lengths than the other two.

List of symbols and notation

The following notation will be used in all Edexcel examinations.

$\in$	is an element of
$\notin$	is not an element of
$\{x_1, x_2, \ldots\}$	the set with elements $x_1, x_2, \ldots$
$\{x : \ldots\}$	the set of all x such that $\ldots$
$\mathrm{n}(A)$	the number of elements in set A
$\emptyset$	the empty set
$\mathscr{E}$	the universal set
A'	the complement of the set A
$\mathbb{N}$	the set of natural numbers, $\{1, 2, 3, \ldots\}$
$\mathbb{Z}$	the set of integers, $\{0, \pm 1, \pm 2, \pm 3, \ldots\}$
$\mathbb{Z}^+$	the set of positive integers, $\{1, 2, 3, \ldots\}$
$\mathbb{Z}_n$	the set of integers modulo n, $\{0, 1, 2, \ldots, n-1\}$
$\mathbb{Q}$	the set of rational numbers $\left\{\dfrac{p}{q} : p \in \mathbb{Z}, q \in \mathbb{Z}^+\right\}$
$\mathbb{Q}^+$	the set of positive rational numbers, $\{x \in \mathbb{Q} : x > 0\}$
$\mathbb{Q}_0^+$	the set of positive rational numbers and zero, $\{x \in \mathbb{Q} : x \geqslant 0\}$
$\mathbb{R}$	the set of real numbers
$\mathbb{R}^+$	the set of positive real numbers, $\{x \in \mathbb{R} : x > 0\}$
$\mathbb{R}_0^+$	the set of positive real numbers and zero, $\{x \in \mathbb{R} : x \geqslant 0\}$
$\mathbb{C}$	the set of complex numbers
(x, y)	the ordered pair x, y
$A \times B$	the cartesian product of sets A and B, $A \times B = \{(a, b) : a \in A, b \in B\}$
$\subseteq$	is a subset of
$\subset$	is a proper subset of
$\cup$	union
$\cap$	intersection
$[a, b]$	the closed interval, $\{x \in \mathbb{R} : a \leqslant x \leqslant b\}$
$[a, b), [a, b[$	the interval $\{x \in \mathbb{R} : a \leqslant x < b\}$
$(a, b],]a, b]$	the interval $\{x \in \mathbb{R} : a < x \leqslant b\}$
$(a, b),]a, b[$	the open interval $\{x \in \mathbb{R} : a < x < b\}$
$y\,R\,x$	y is related to x by the relation R
$y \sim x$	y is equivalent to x, in the context of some equivalence relation
$=$	is equal to
$\neq$	is not equal to
$\equiv$	is identical to *or* is congruent to

$\approx$	is approximately equal to
$\cong$	is isomorphic to
$\propto$	is proportional to
$<$	is less than
$\leqslant$, $\ngtr$	is less than or equal to, is not greater than
$>$	is greater than
$\geqslant$, $\nless$	is greater than or equal to, is not less than
∞	infinity
$p \wedge q$	p and q
$p \vee q$	p or q (or both)
$\sim p$	not p
$p \Rightarrow q$	p implies q (if p then q)
$p \Leftarrow q$	p implied by q (if q then p)
$p \Leftrightarrow q$	p implies and is implied by q (p is equivalent to q)
$\exists$	there exists
$\forall$	for all
$a + b$	a plus b
$a - b$	a minus b
$a \times b$, ab, $a.b$	a multiplied by b
$a \div b$, $\dfrac{a}{b}$, a/b	a divided by b
$\displaystyle\sum_{i=1}^{n} a_i$	$a_1 + a_2 + \ldots + a_n$
$\displaystyle\prod_{i=1}^{n} a_i$	$a_1 \times a_2 \times \ldots \times a_n$
$\sqrt{a}$	the positive square root of a
$|a|$	the modulus of a
$n!$	n factorial
$\dbinom{n}{r}$	the binomial coefficient $\dfrac{n!}{r!(n-r)!}$ for $n \in \mathbb{Z}^+$ $\dfrac{n(n-1)\ldots(n-r+1)}{r!}$ for $n \in \mathbb{Q}$
$f(x)$	the value of the function f at x
$f : A \rightarrow B$	f is a function under which each element of set A has an image in set B
$f : x \mapsto y$	the function f maps the element x to the element y
f^{-1}	the inverse function of the function f
$g \circ f$, gf	the composite function of f and g which is defined by $(g \circ f)(x)$ or $gf(x) = g(f(x))$
$\displaystyle\lim_{x \to a} f(x)$	the limit of $f(x)$ as x tends to a
Δx, δx	an increment of x
$\dfrac{dy}{dx}$	the derivative of y with respect to x
$\dfrac{d^n y}{dx^n}$	the nth derivative of y with respect to x

$f'(x), f''(x), \ldots f^{(n)}(x)$	the first, second, $\ldots$ nth derivatives of $f(x)$ with respect to x
$\displaystyle\int y\,\mathrm{d}x$	the indefinite integral of y with respect to x
$\displaystyle\int_a^b y\,\mathrm{d}x$	the definite integral of y with respect to x between the limits $x = a$ and $x = b$
$\dfrac{\partial V}{\partial x}$	the partial derivative of V with respect to x
$\dot{x}, \ddot{x}, \ldots$	the first, second, $\ldots$ derivatives of x with respect to t
e	base of natural logarithms
e^x, $\exp x$	exponential function of x
$\log_a x$	logarithm to the base a of x
$\ln x$, $\log_e x$	natural logarithm of x
$\lg x$, $\log_{10} x$	logarithm of to base 10
sin, cos, tan cosec, sec, cot	the circular functions
arcsin, arccos, arctan arccosec, arcsec, arccot	the inverse circular functions
sinh, cosh, tanh cosech, sech, coth	the hyperbolic functions
arsinh, arcosh, artanh, arcosech, arsech, arcoth	the inverse hyperbolic functions
i, j	square root of -1
z	a complex number, $z = x + iy$
Re z	the real part of z, Re $z = x$
Im z	the imaginary part of z, Im $z = y$
$|z|$	the modulus of z, $|z| = \sqrt{(x^2 + y^2)}$
arg z	the argument of z, arg $z = \arctan\dfrac{y}{x}$
z^*	the complex conjugate of z, $x - iy$
$\mathbf{M}$	a matrix $\mathbf{M}$
$\mathbf{M}^{-1}$	the inverse of the matrix $\mathbf{M}$
$\mathbf{M}^{\mathrm{T}}$	the transpose of the matrix $\mathbf{M}$
det $\mathbf{M}$, $|\mathbf{M}|$	the determinant of the square matrix $\mathbf{M}$
$\mathbf{a}$	the vector $\mathbf{a}$
$\overrightarrow{AB}$	the vector represented in magnitude and direction by the directed line segment AB
$\hat{\mathbf{a}}$	a unit vector in the direction of $\mathbf{a}$
$\mathbf{i}, \mathbf{j}, \mathbf{k}$	unit vectors in the directions of the cartesian coordinate axes
$|\mathbf{a}|$, a	the magnitude of $\mathbf{a}$
$|\overrightarrow{AB}|$, AB	the magnitude of $\overrightarrow{AB}$
$\mathbf{a} \cdot \mathbf{b}$	the scalar product of $\mathbf{a}$ and $\mathbf{b}$
$\mathbf{a} \times \mathbf{b}$	the vector product of $\mathbf{a}$ and $\mathbf{b}$

A, B, C, etc	events
$A \cup B$	union of the events A and B
$A \cap B$	intersection of the events A and B
$\mathrm{P}(A)$	probability of the event A
A'	complement of the event A
$\mathrm{P}(A\vert B)$	probability of the event A conditional on the event B
X, Y, R, etc.	random variables
x, y, r, etc.	values of the random variables X, Y, R, etc
$x_1, x_2 \ldots$	observations
$f_1, f_2, \ldots$	frequencies with which the observations $x_1, x_2, \ldots$ occur
$\mathrm{p}(x)$	probability function $\mathrm{P}(X = x)$ of the discrete random variable X
$p_1, p_2, \ldots$	probabilities of the values $x_1, x_2, \ldots$ of the discrete random variable X
$\mathrm{f}(x), \mathrm{g}(x), \ldots$	the value of the probability density function of a continuous random variable X
$\mathrm{F}(x), \mathrm{G}(x), \ldots$	the value of the (cumulative) distribution function $\mathrm{P}(X \leqslant x)$ of a continuous random variable X
$\mathrm{E}(X)$	expectation of the random variable X
$\mathrm{E}[\mathrm{g}(X)]$	expectation of $\mathrm{g}(X)$
$\mathrm{Var}(X)$	variance of the random variable X
$\mathrm{G}(t)$	probability generating function for a random variable which takes the values 0, 1, 2, $\ldots$
$\mathrm{B}(n, p)$	binomial distribution with parameters n and p
$\mathrm{N}(\mu, \sigma^2)$	normal distribution with mean μ and variance σ^2
μ	population mean
σ^2	population variance
σ	population standard deviation
$\bar{x}, m$	sample mean
$s^2, \hat{\sigma}^2$	unbiased estimate of population variance from a sample, $$s^2 = \frac{1}{n-1} \sum (x_i - \bar{x})^2$$
ϕ	probability density function of the standardised normal variable with distribution $\mathrm{N}(0, 1)$
Φ	corresponding cumulative distribution function
ρ	product-moment correlation coefficient for a population
r	product-moment correlation coefficient for a sample
$\mathrm{Cov}\,(X, Y)$	covariance of X and Y

Index